Mifflin
Harcourt

Curious George by Margret and H.A. Rey. Copyright © 2010 by Houghton Mifflin Harcourt Publishing Company. All rights reserved. The character Curious George®, including without limitation the character's name and the character's likenesses, are registered trademarks of Houghton Mifflin Harcourt Publishing Company.

Copyright © 2015 by Houghton Mifflin Harcourt Publishing Company

Printed in the U.S.A.

ISBN 978-0-544-29562-9

11 12 13 14   0607   23 22 21 20 19
4500770699   D E F G

Critical Area Measurement and Data

 Common Core **CRITICAL AREA** Representing, relating, and operating on whole numbers, initially with sets of objects

Key: Major Clusters: ■   Supporting Clusters: □   Additional Clusters: ○

Table of Contents

Chapter 11   Measurement

Domain: Measurement and Data   K.MD

Common Core MATHEMATICAL PRACTICES

MP1 Make sense of problems and persevere in solving them.

MP2 Reason abstractly and quantitatively.

MP3 Construct viable arguments and critique the reasoning of others.

MP4 Model with mathematics.

MP5 Use appropriate tools strategically.

MP6 Attend to precision.

MP7 Look for and make use of structure.

MP8 Look for and express regularity in repeated reasoning.

Measurement and Data

 CRITICAL AREA Representing, relating, and operating on whole numbers, initially with sets of objects

Common Core PROFESSIONAL DEVELOPMENT

See Teaching for Depth, 645C and 683C.

See Mathematical Practices in every lesson.

Digital Resources

FOR LEARNING...

 Interactive Student Edition

- Immerses students in an interactive, multi-sensory math environment
- Enhances learning with scaffolded, interactive instruction and just-in-time feedback
- Provides audio reinforcement for each lesson
- Makes learning a two-way experience, using a variety of interactive tools

FOR ASSESSMENT AND INTERVENTION...

 Personal Math Trainer

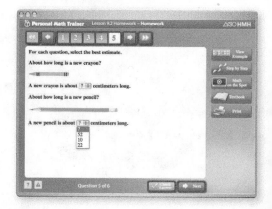

- Creates a personalized learning path for each student
- Provides opportunities for practice, homework, and assessment
- Includes worked-out examples and helpful video support
- Offers targeted intervention and extra support to build proficiency and understanding

FOR DAILY MATH TUTORING...

 Math on the Spot Videos

- Models good problem-solving thinking in every lesson
- Engages students through interesting animations and fun characters
- Builds student problem-solving proficiency and confidence
- Builds the skills needed for success on the Common Core Assessments

FOR SIMPLICITY...

HMH Player App

It's For Students ...

- Content is available online, offline, and on-the-go!
- Students are engaged in class, at home, and anywhere in between for uninterrupted instruction
- Raise a Hand for instant student-teacher-student communication

... And For Teachers!

- Teachers can monitor student progress in real time
- Lesson customization features allow teachers to deliver personalized learning
- Plan your lessons, make assignments, and view results from the convenience of your classroom, at home, or on-the-go
- Supports blended learning through anywhere digital instruction

FOR TEACHING...

Digital Management System

- Manage online all program content and components
- Search for and select resources based on Common Core State Standards
- Identify resources based on student ability and needs
- View and assign student lessons, practice, assessments, and more

Professional Development Videos

- Learn more about the Common Core and Common Core content
- See first-hand the integration of the Mathematical Practices
- Watch students engaged in a productive struggle

Critical Area Pacing Chart

Introduction	Chapters	Assessment	Total
Vocabulary Reader		Performance Assessment	
1 day	8 days	1 day	10 days

1 READ

Plants all Around

Objective Use literature to reinforce measurement concepts.

Genre Nonfiction

Domain: Measurement and Data

▶ **Preparing to Read** Refer children to the story cover and read the title. Ask what they think the story will be about.

Explain to children that they will read the story together, using the pictures to solve math problems on each page. Tell children that they will read the story again and learn some fun facts to answer science questions about plants.

▶ **Story Vocabulary** leaves, flowers, carrots, roots, cattails, stems

▶ **Reading the Math Story**
Pages 637–640

Have children compare the lengths or heights of the plants or plant parts.

- **How can you tell which leaf is longer?**
  I can see which leaf stretches farther across the page.

- **How can you tell which flower is shorter?**
  I can look at both flowers and compare.

- **How can you tell which carrot is longer?**
  I can look at both carrots to see which one goes deeper.

Explain that leaves, flowers, roots, and stems are necessary to help plants grow. Discuss how all of the plants in this story are similar.

written by Tami Morton

Representing, relating, and operating on whole numbers, initially with sets of objects

six hundred thirty-seven **637**

Two leaves fall from a tree.
Circle the leaf that is longer.

638 six hundred thirty-eight Why do plants have leaves?

Two flowers grow near a wall.
Circle the flower that is shorter.

Why do plants have flowers? six hundred thirty-nine **639**

These carrots grow under the ground.
Circle the carrot that is longer.

640 six hundred forty Why do plants have roots?

Cattails can be short or tall.
Circle the two cattails that are about the same height.

Why do plants have stems? six hundred forty-one **641**

Check children's work.

One leaf is shorter than the other leaf.
Draw a leaf that is about the same length as the shorter leaf.

642 six hundred forty-two How are all these plants the same?

Name _____

Write About the Story WRITE Math

Draw a purple flower. Make it shorter than the orange flower and taller than the yellow flower.
Check children's work.

Vocabulary Review
longer   taller
shorter   same

six hundred forty-three **643**

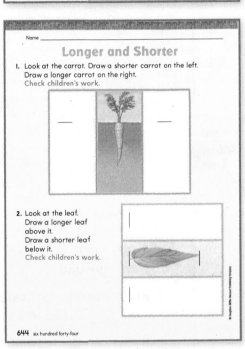

Name _____

Longer and Shorter

1. Look at the carrot. Draw a shorter carrot on the left. Draw a longer carrot on the right.
Check children's work.

2. Look at the leaf. Draw a longer leaf above it. Draw a shorter leaf below it.
Check children's work.

644 six hundred forty-four

Pages 641 and 642

Children should understand the story progression. Have them share how they solved each problem.

- **How can you tell which cattails are about the same height?** I can compare them to see which look to be about the same height.

- **On page 642, how can you draw a leaf that is about the same length as the shorter leaf?** I can find the shorter leaf and draw another leaf that stretches the same distance across the page.

2 RESPOND

Write About the Story

Page 643

WRITE Math Have children draw a purple flower that is shorter than the orange flower and taller than the yellow flower.

- **How can you draw a flower that is shorter than the orange flower and taller than the yellow flower?** I can draw a flower that goes higher than the yellow flower but not as high as the orange flower.

You may wish to have volunteers share their pictures with the class.

▶ **Math Vocabulary** longer, shorter, taller, same

Do the Math • Longer and Shorter

Page 644

WRITE Math In this activity, children are given an object as a reference point. They must draw an object that is longer and an object that is shorter.

 Connections to Science

Read the story again as children follow along. For each page, tell children one of the facts below about plants. Have children look at the story pictures again and discuss the Science questions on each page.

FLOWER Facts:

- Flowers are the easiest part of the plant to see.
- There are over 240,000 kinds of flowering plants.
- California poppies are flowers that close at night and open in the morning.

ROOT Facts:

- Roots, such as carrots, are plant parts that stay underground.
- Roots absorb the water and other things that a plant needs from the soil.
- Roots can grow to be very large.

LEAF Facts:

- Leaves are on a plant's stem.
- Plants use their leaves to make food.
- Plants also use their leaves to get rid of extra water.

STEM Facts:

- A plant's stem helps keep it upright.
- The stem also carries food to all parts of the plant.
- Cattail stems are starchy, like potatoes, and can be eaten.

Real World Project

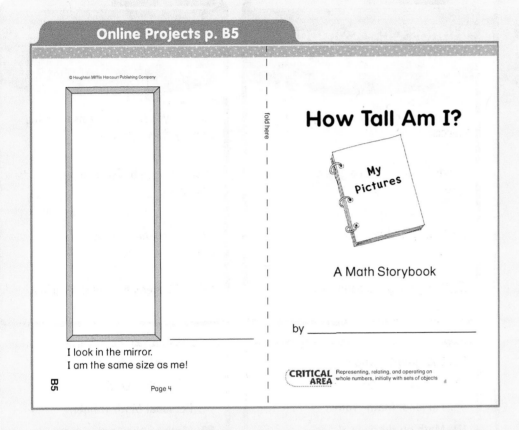

© Houghton Mifflin Harcourt Publishing Company

I look in the mirror.
I am the same size as me!

B5

Page 4

How Tall Am I?

My Pictures

A Math Storybook

by _____

CRITICAL AREA — Representing, relating, and operating on whole numbers, initially with sets of objects

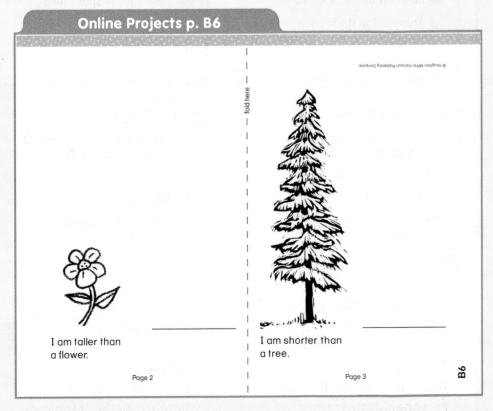

© Houghton Mifflin Harcourt Publishing Company

I am taller than a flower.

Page 2

I am shorter than a tree.

Page 3

B6

My Math Project Storybook

How Tall Am I?

Objective Compare heights using the terms *shorter*, *taller*, and *same*.

Materials Online Projects pp. B5–B6

Help children fold their pages to make a storybook. Tell children that they will draw pictures to show how tall they are compared to other objects.

On page 2, children draw a picture of themselves to show that they are taller than a flower. On page 3, they draw a picture to show that they are shorter than a tree. On page 4, children draw a picture to show that they are the same height as their reflection.

• **Are you shorter or taller than a flower?**
taller

• **Are you shorter or taller than the tree?**
shorter

Once children have completed the pages, have them turn back to their storybook covers. Encourage them to draw a picture that tells about their story. You may want to encourage children to do further research on measurement in the real world by using different types of media (library, online, etc.).

Have children share their work with the class, and then take their storybooks home to share with family members.

Performance Assessment You can use this project as a means of assessing a child's understanding of the concepts and skills found in this Critical Area.

Chapter At A Glance

Domain: Measurement and Data

Chapter Essential Question How can comparing objects help you measure them?

Use the *GO Math! Planning Guide* for correlations, mathematical practices information, and more.

	1 Day **LESSON 11.1** ○ K.MD.A.2	**0.5 Day** **LESSON 11.2** ○ K.MD.A.2	**0.5 Day** **LESSON 11.3** ○ K.MD.A.2
Lesson At A Glance	**Hands On • Compare Lengths........ 649A**	**Hands On • Compare Heights........ 655A**	**Problem Solving • Direct Comparison** **............... 661A**
Essential Question	How can you compare the lengths of two objects?	How can you compare the heights of two objects?	How can you solve problems using the strategy *draw a picture?*
Objective	Directly compare the lengths of two objects.	Directly compare the heights of two objects.	Solve problems by using the strategy *draw a picture.*
Vocabulary	**longer, same length, shorter**	**same height, taller,** shorter	longer, same height, same length, shorter, taller
ELL Strategy	**ELL** Strategy • Identify Relationships	**ELL** Strategy • Identify Relationships	**ELL** Strategy • Develop Meanings

GO DIGITAL Go online to access all your chapter resources

www.thinkcentral.com

11.1 *i*Student Edition	11.2 *i*Student Edition	11.3 *i*Student Edition
11.1 *e*Teacher Edition	11.2 *e*Teacher Edition	11.3 *e*Teacher Edition
Personal Math Trainer	Personal Math Trainer	Personal Math Trainer
Math on the Spot Video	Math on the Spot Video	Math on the Spot Video
Animated Math Models	Animated Math Models	
*i*Tools	*i*Tools	
HMH Mega Math		

Print Resources

11.1 Student Edition	11.2 Student Edition	11.3 Student Edition
11.1 Practice and Homework (in the *Student Edition*)	11.2 Practice and Homework (in the *Student Edition*)	11.3 Practice and Homework (in the *Student Edition*)
11.1 Reteach (in the *Chapter Resources*)	11.2 Reteach (in the *Chapter Resources*)	11.3 Reteach (in the *Chapter Resources*)
11.1 Enrich (in the *Chapter Resources*)	11.2 Enrich (in the *Chapter Resources*)	11.3 Enrich (in the *Chapter Resources*)
Grab-and-Go™ Centers Kit	Grab-and-Go™ Centers Kit	Grab-and-Go™ Centers Kit

Before the Chapter	**During the Lesson**	**After the Chapter**
✓ **Show What You Know**	✓ **Share and Show**	✓ **Chapter Review/Test**
• Prerequisite Skills Activities • Personal Math Trainer	• Reteach • Mid-Chapter Checkpoint • Personal Math Trainer • Reteach Activity (online)	• Reteach • Personal Math Trainer • Reteach Activity (online)

RtI Response to Intervention

I Day

LESSON 11.4 ◯ K.MD.A.2

Hands On • Compare Weights 667A

How can you compare the weights of two objects?

Directly compare the weights of two objects.

heavier, lighter, same weight

ELL **Strategy** • Identify Relationships

I Day

LESSON 11.5 ◯ K.MD.A.I

Length, Height, and Weight 673A

How can you describe several ways to measure one object?

Describe several measurable attributes of a single object.

heavier, lighter, longer, shorter, taller

ELL **Strategy** • Scaffold Language

Teacher Notes

11.4 *i*Student Edition

11.4 *e*Teacher Edition

Personal Math Trainer

Math on the Spot Video

Animated Math Models

HMH Mega Math

11.5 *i*Student Edition

11.5 *e*Teacher Edition

Personal Math Trainer

Math on the Spot Video

✓ Chapter 11 Test

11.4 Student Edition

11.4 Practice and Homework
(in the *Student Edition*)

11.4 Reteach (in the *Chapter Resources*)

11.4 Enrich (in the *Chapter Resources*)

Grab-and-Go™ Centers Kit

11.5 Student Edition

11.5 Practice and Homework
(in the *Student Edition*)

11.5 Reteach (in the *Chapter Resources*)

11.5 Enrich (in the *Chapter Resources*)

Grab-and-Go™ Centers Kit

GO DIGITAL **Resources** *www.thinkcentral.com*

 Interactive Student Edition

Personal Math Trainer

 Math on the Spot Video

 Animated Math Models

 ✓ Assessment

 HMH Mega Math

 *i*Tools

 Multimedia *e*Glossary

Professional Development Videos

PROFESSIONAL DEVELOPMENT # Teaching for Depth

Steven J. Leinwand
Principal Research Analyst,
American Institutes for Research (AIR)
Washington, D.C.

Length and Height

In the context of learning about length, children should be guided to make comparisons between objects that explicitly display the attribute of length and use terms such as *same as, shorter than,* and *longer than*.

- Aligning objects one below the other and comparing their lengths using language as described above is an example of direct measurement of length.

The red pencil is shorter.

The blue pencil is longer.

- Like length, height is the measurement of distance between two points.

- Comparisons of height are described by using words like *taller, shorter, higher,* and *lower*.

Some children may discover that objects can have more than one measurable attribute.

Weight

Weight is the measurement of the pull of gravity on an object.

- A starting place for teaching children about weight is to give them an opportunity to hold objects in their hands to compare them.

- When comparing weights, use terms such as *heavier, lighter,* or *the same*.

- Ordering objects according to weight helps build understanding of the concept.

Common Core ## Mathematical Practices

For young children to **reason abstractly and quantitatively** in the context of measurement, they need many experiences physically comparing objects, discussing their comparisons of objects, and measuring objects with nonstandard units. When children measure a pair of scissors as 19 cubes long and measure an envelope as 15 cubes long, they use reasoning to make a conclusion based on this quantitative information. How they make sense of these quantities provides a foundation for how children will interpret measurements when they are using standard units.

Nonstandard Units

Children's first experience in measuring the length of objects should be with nonstandard units, particularly units that can be snapped together (e.g., connecting cubes) or easily placed side by side (e.g., square tiles).

From the Research

❝Classroom research points to the importance of helping children go beyond procedural competence to learn about the mathematical underpinnings of measure so that procedures and concepts are mutually bootstrapped.❞
(Lehrer, 2003, p. 190)

 Professional Development Videos:
Measurement and Geometry, Grades K–2, Segment 5

Daily Classroom Management

 Differentiated Instruction

Whole Group	Small Group	Whole Group
1 ENGAGE	**3** EXPLAIN	**4** ELABORATE
2 EXPLORE	✓ QUICK CHECK	**5** EVALUATE

0 to 1 correct  RtI

INTERVENE
These children need lesson support.

2 correct

ON LEVEL
These children are ready to begin independent practice.

Advanced

ENRICH
These children are ready for enrichment.

Extra Support

Teachers may need to decelerate the rate at which new material is introduced.
- Reteach (in the *Chapter Resources*)
- **ELL** Activity

GO DIGITAL
- Strategic Intervention Guide
- Intensive Intervention Guide
- Personal Math Trainer

On Level

- Practice and Homework (in the *Student Edition*)
- **ELL** Activity

GO DIGITAL
- HMH Mega Math
- *i*Tools

Enrich

Teachers may need to accelerate the rate at which new material is introduced.
- Advanced Learners Activity
- Enrich (in the *Chapter Resources*)
- Extend the Project
- **ELL** Activity

GO DIGITAL
- HMH Mega Math
- *i*Tools

WHAT ARE THE OTHER CHILDREN DOING?

Differentiated Centers Kit

The kit provides literature, games, and activities for use every day.

Strategies for
English Language Learners

by Elizabeth Jiménez
*CEO, GEMAS Consulting
Professional Expert on
English Learner Education
Bilingual Education and Dual Language
Pomona, California*

The **Identify Relationships Strategy** makes connections between new concepts and something familiar. Identifying the relationship between concepts and words helps build children's confidence in using mathematical terms.

Benefit to English Language Learners

Using the Identify Relationships Strategy encourages children to use their prior knowledge and personal experiences to connect to new concepts and words. It is beneficial to English Language Learners because:

- children increase their confidence with new concepts.

- knowledge of new words is established before they are expected to use them independently.

- children realize how much they already know.

From the Research

"New knowledge is best learned and retained when it can be linked to existing 'funds of knowledge' (Moll et al. 1990) so new content should be introduced through its relationship to an already understood concept."

(Annette Zehler, *Working with English Language Learners, 1994.*)

Planning for Instruction

Mathematics and the language necessary to talk about it are more easily learned and incorporated into a child's knowledge when they can be linked to previous knowledge. This linking can be accomplished with visual clues, by comparing relationships between objects, or by simple sorting activities.

Some of the comparison vocabulary in this chapter includes:

- heavier and lighter,

- longer, shorter, and taller, and

- same height, same length, and same weight.

Children can develop the language for talking about relationships and using comparison language by using various activities. Sorting games, comparing objects for relative size and weight, drawing objects and describing them using the new vocabulary, and choosing objects that fit a definition such as *shorter than* are possible activities to help identify relationships.

When children can use physical objects to learn and demonstrate their knowledge of relationships, it aids in retention. Children will build on their previous vocabulary and will be able to describe and compare objects independently.

Linguistic Note

Because English often follows patterns, children can quickly increase their vocabulary when they identify these patterns. Point out that adjectives such as *short* can be used to compare objects by adding the suffix *–er*. Warn children that not all adjectives will follow this pattern, but encourage them to try it with new words: *fast, faster; dark, darker,* etc.

Developing Math Language

Chapter Vocabulary

heavier having a greater weight

lighter having a lesser weight

longer having a greater length

shorter having a lesser length or height

taller having a greater height

same height not taller and not shorter; having heights that match

same length not longer and not shorter; having lengths that match

same weight not heavier and not lighter; having weights that match

GO DIGITAL
• Interactive Student Edition
• Multimedia eGlossary

ELL Vocabulary Activity

See **ELL** *Activity Guide for leveled activities.*

Objective Understand the math term *taller*.
Materials Vocabulary Card for *taller*
(see *eTeacher Resources*)

Ask a child to stand next to you. Show the card for *taller*. Say: **I am taller than [Samantha].** Then have two children stand up. Ask, **Who is taller?** Have children answer. Repeat activity until all children have a turn.

Practice vocabulary by using questioning strategies:

Beginning
• Show children two cups that are different heights. **Which cup is taller?**

Intermediate
• Show children an object. Have children find another object in the classroom that is taller. Ask them to use the term *taller* in a sentence about the object they find.

Advanced
• How can you tell whether an object or a person is taller than another object or person? Accept reasonable answers.

Vocabulary Strategy • Graphic Organizer

Materials Vocabulary Cards (see *eTeacher Resources*)

• Post new words that children may need to practice on the word wall as each lesson is introduced.

• Practice these words as a "warm up" activity before the lessons.

• When one of the words appears in the lesson, reinforce it by pointing to it on the word wall.

Add these words to the word wall.

longer, shorter, taller,

heavier, lighter,

same length,

same height,

same weight

longer	shorter

Review Prerequisite Skills

RtI Activities

TIER 2

The Same Length

Objective Represent ideas of length.
Materials two strips of construction paper of the same length, various classroom objects

Children's initial understanding of measurement is much like their understanding of shape. Their judgments are based on how the objects look.

Display the strips of paper that are the same length, one green and one blue, but do not left-align them.

- **Is the green strip longer than the blue strip, or are the strips the same length?** the same length

Some children may not yet conserve length and may think that one strip is longer than the other.

Have children use the strips to find classroom objects that are the same length as the strips. Work with children to reinforce the importance of aligning the objects with the strips.

TIER 2

How Heavy?

Objective Initiate discussion of weight.
Materials a child's full backpack, a small bag with a few crayons inside

Show the backpack and bag.

- **How are these items alike? How are they different?** Children may say that both hold things, but the backpack is bigger or can hold more than the bag.

Let several children lift the backpack and then the bag.

- **What do they feel like when you lift them?** Children may say that the backpack is heavy or that it is harder to lift than the bag.

- **What are some things that are easy to lift? What are some things that are hard to lift?** Children will probably name small objects as being easy to lift and larger ones as harder to lift.

Tell children that they will learn more about weight and use words such as *heavier* and *lighter* as they complete lessons in the chapter.

Measurement and Data

Common Core

Making Content Connections

Across Grades

In Chapter 11 of Grade K, children build upon their understanding of comparing numbers (K.CC.C) as they begin to describe and compare measurable attributes. Children build on their knowledge that each successive number name refers to a quantity that is one larger (K.CC.B.4c), and identify whether the number of objects in one group is *greater than*, *less than*, or *equal to* the number of objects in another group (K.CC.C.6). When children directly compare and describe two objects with a measurable attribute in common, they know which object has "more of" or "less of" the attribute, and can describe the difference (K.MD.A.2). Children use appropriate math vocabulary such as "taller than," "shorter than," "heavier than," and "lighter than" to compare objects.

After Grade K, children will apply their understanding of measurable attributes as they learn to measure length using a variety of tools, such as indirect measurement and iterated length. Children will further study measurement as they learn to tell and write time from an analog clock.

Connect to the Major Work

The major work in Grade K is comparing numbers, K.CC.C. In Lessons 11.1–11.4, children compare numbers representing lengths, heights, and weights. Children will learn appropriate terms ("taller than," "shorter than," "heavier than," and "lighter than") for these comparisons, connecting to previous knowledge of "greater than" and "less than."

Common Core State Standards
Across the Grades

Before	In Grade K	After
• Compare lengths. • Compare weights.	**Domain: Measurement and Data** ○ **Cluster A:** Describe and compare measurable attributes. **Standards: K.MD.A.1, K.MD.A.2**	**Domain: Measurement and Data** **Cluster A:** Measure lengths indirectly and by iterating length units. **Standards: 1.MD.A.1, 1.MD.A.2** **Cluster B:** Tell and write time. **Standard: 1.MD.B.3**

For the full text of the Common Core State Standards, see the A page of each lesson or the *Common Core State Standards Correlations* in the *Planning Guide*. For the full text of the Standards for Mathematical Practices, see *Mathematical Practices in GO Math!* in the *Planning Guide*.

Curious About Math with Curious George

A playground is an area designed for children to play.
- **Which person on the park bench is bigger?** the person on the left

Additional facts about playgrounds:

- **There are many child-sized spaces on a playground.**

- **Playgrounds provide a fun and safe place to play.**

Ask the following questions to guide children to an answer.

- **Which slide is longer?** Accept reasonable answers.

- **Which covered area is taller?** the one on the right

Chapter 11 Measurement

Curious About Math with Curious George

A playground is an area designed for children to play.
- Which person on the park bench is bigger? the person on the left

Intervention Options   RtI   Response to Intervention

Use Show What You Know, Lesson Quick Check, and Assessments to diagnose children's intervention levels.

TIER 1	TIER 2	TIER 3	ENRICHMENT
On-Level Intervention	**Strategic Intervention**	**Intensive Intervention**	**Independent Activities**
For children who are generally at grade level but need early intervention with the lesson concepts, use:	For children who need small group instruction to review concepts and skills needed for the chapter, use:	For children who need one-on-one instruction to build foundational skills for the chapter, use:	For children who successfully complete lessons, use:

TIER 1 — On-Level Intervention:
- Reteach (in the *Chapter Resources*)
- Personal Math Trainer
- Tier 1 Activity online

TIER 2 — Strategic Intervention:
- Strategic Intervention Guide
- Personal Math Trainer
- Prerequisite Skills Activities
- Tier 2 Activity online

TIER 3 — Intensive Intervention:
- Intensive Intervention Guide
- Personal Math Trainer
- Prerequisite Skills Activities

ENRICHMENT — Independent Activities:

 Grab-and-Go!

Differentiated Centers Kit

- Advanced Learners Activity for every lesson

- Enrich Activity (in the *Chapter Resources*)

 HMH Mega Math

Name _____

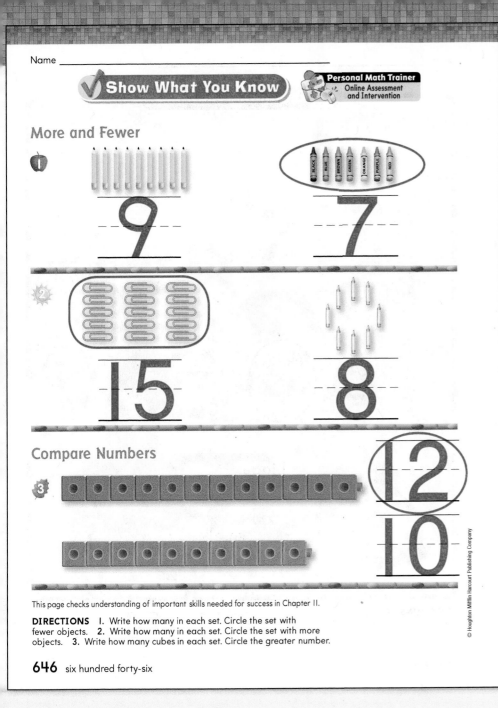

✓ Show What You Know

Personal Math Trainer
Online Assessment
and Intervention

More and Fewer

① 9   7

② 15   8

Compare Numbers

③ 12
10

This page checks understanding of important skills needed for success in Chapter 11.

DIRECTIONS 1. Write how many in each set. Circle the set with fewer objects. 2. Write how many in each set. Circle the set with more objects. 3. Write how many cubes in each set. Circle the greater number.

© Houghton Mifflin Harcourt Publishing Company

646 six hundred forty-six

Assessing Prior Knowledge

Have children complete on their own **Show What You Know.** Tested items are the prerequisite skills of this chapter.

Diagnostic Interview Task

The alternative interview tasks below evaluate children's understanding of each **Show What You Know** skill. The diagnostic chart may be used for intervention on prerequisite skills.

Materials erasers, connecting cubes, Numeral Cards (8–15) (see *eTeacher Resources*), two-color counters

For evaluation checklist see *Chapter Resource Book.*

Display a set of four erasers and a set of six erasers. Have the child count the erasers in each set.

• **Which set has fewer erasers?** the set of four erasers

Display 14 counters arranged in a circle and 9 counters in a rectangular array. Have the child count the counters in each set.

• **Which set has more counters?** the set with 14 counters

Display a 10-cube train and an 8-cube train. Have the child place the matching numeral card next to each set.

• **Which number is greater?** 10

✓ Show What You Know • Diagnostic Assessment

Use to determine if children need intervention for the chapter's prerequisite skills.

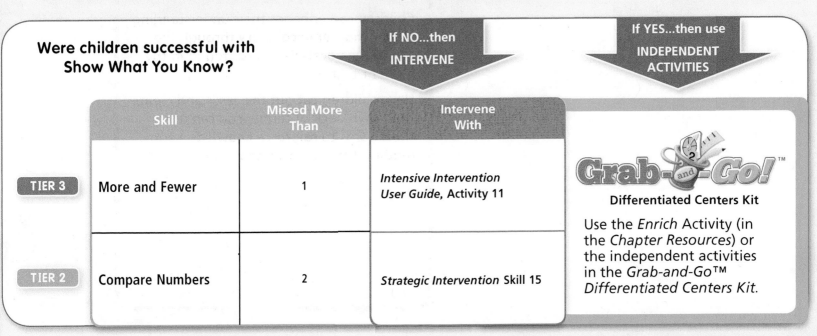

Were children successful with Show What You Know?

If NO...then INTERVENE

If YES...then use INDEPENDENT ACTIVITIES

	Skill	Missed More Than	Intervene With
TIER 3	More and Fewer	1	*Intensive Intervention User Guide,* Activity 11
TIER 2	Compare Numbers	2	*Strategic Intervention* Skill 15

Grab-and-Go!™
Differentiated Centers Kit

Use the *Enrich* Activity (in the *Chapter Resources*) or the independent activities in the *Grab-and-Go™ Differentiated Centers Kit.*

Chapter 11

Introduce the Chapter

Vocabulary Builder

Children use multiple strategies to develop grade-appropriate vocabulary.

Have children complete the activities on the page by working alone or with partners.

Look at the page with children.

- **Are there more flowers in the bigger pot or the smaller pot?** smaller pot

Discuss with children that size is not necessarily an indication of weight or quantity. For example, the smaller pot contains more flowers than the bigger pot; the spade is smaller than a flower outside the window, but the spade is heavier.

Have children draw a bigger picture on the wall.

Name _____

Vocabulary Builder

bigger

smaller

DIRECTIONS Are there more flowers in the bigger pot or the smaller pot? Circle to show the pot with more flowers.

GO DIGITAL • Interactive Student Edition • Multimedia eGlossary

© Houghton Mifflin Harcourt Publishing Company

Vocabulary Cards

Children can enhance their understanding of **key chapter vocabulary** through the use of the vocabulary cards found in the Student Edition.

Have children cut out the cards and create their own deck of terms. You can use these cards to **reinforce knowledge** and **reading across the content areas**.

Connecting Cube Challenge

START

END

© Houghton Mifflin Harcourt Publishing Company

DIRECTIONS Take turns with a partner tossing the number cube. Move your marker that number of spaces. If a player lands on a cube, he or she takes a cube for making a cube train. At the end of the game, players compare cube trains. Each player identifies the number of cubes in his or her cube train. If one player has a greater number of cubes, partners should identify that as the larger quantity of cubes.

MATERIALS game markers, number cube (1–6), connecting cubes

648 six hundred forty-eight

Game Connecting Cube Challenge

▶ **Using the Game**

Set up a game center in the classroom. Include the *Connecting Cube Challenge* and the materials needed to play.

Materials game markers, number cube 1–6, connecting cubes

Take turns with a partner tossing the number cube. Move your marker that number of spaces.

If a player lands on a cube, he or she takes a cube for making a cube train. At the end of the game, players compare cube trains.

Each player identifies the number of cubes in his or her cube train. Have players compare their cube trains to see which one is longer.

Chapter Resources

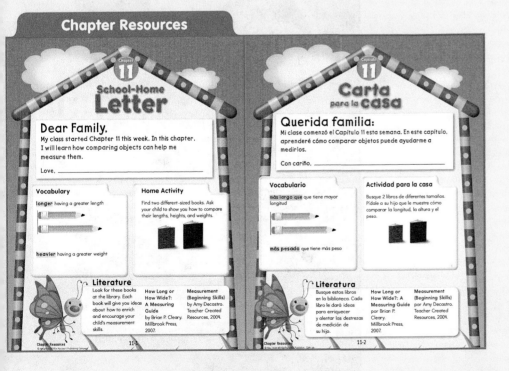

School-Home Letter available in English and Spanish in the *Chapter Resources*. Multiple languages available online at *www.thinkcentral.com*

The letter provides families with an overview of the math in the chapter, math vocabulary, an activity, and literature to read together.

Going Places with *GO Math!* Words

Introduce the Words

Provide child-friendly examples and explanation for the words from this chapter, such as the ones below. Then ask volunteers to explain the math vocabulary in their own words.

- A full backpack is *heavier* than an empty backpack.
- An empty backpack is *lighter* than a full backpack.
- A marker is *longer* than a crayon.
- Parents are usually *taller* than their children.
- The new pencils are all the *same length*.
- The two math books are the *same weight*.

Math Journal  WRITE Math

Have children draw pictures or use numbers to show what the vocabulary words mean. Then ask them to discuss the words and their pictures with a partner.

Going for a Walk in Spring:

What You Need
Each pair needs:

- number cube
- two-color counters for playing pieces
- 5 red connecting cubes
- 5 blue connecting cubes

Show children how to

- roll the number cube
- count and move the correct number of spaces.

ELL Ensure that children understand game terms such as *roll*, *space*, and *count*.

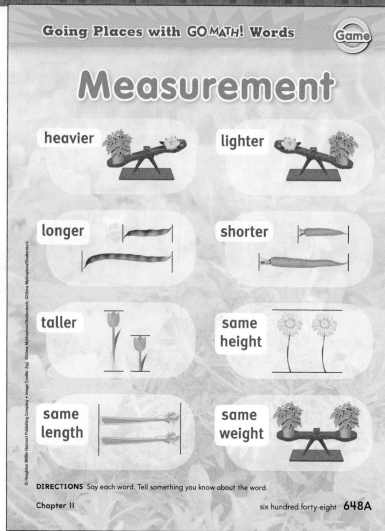

Measurement

heavier

lighter

longer

shorter

taller

same height

same length

same weight

DIRECTIONS Say each word. Tell something you know about the word.

Chapter 11   six hundred forty-eight **648A**

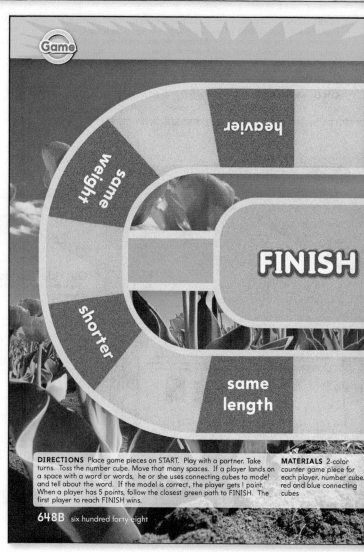

Game

heavier

same weight

shorter

FINISH

same length

DIRECTIONS Place game pieces on START. Play with a partner. Take turns. Toss the number cube. Move that many spaces. If a player lands on a space with a word or words, he or she uses connecting cubes to model and tell about the word. If the model is correct, the player gets 1 point. When a player has 5 points, follow the closest green path to FINISH. The first player to reach FINISH wins.

MATERIALS 2-color counter game piece for each player, number cube, red and blue connecting cubes

648B six hundred forty-eight

The Write Way

DIRECTIONS Draw to show how to compare the length of two objects.
Reflect Be ready to tell about your drawing.

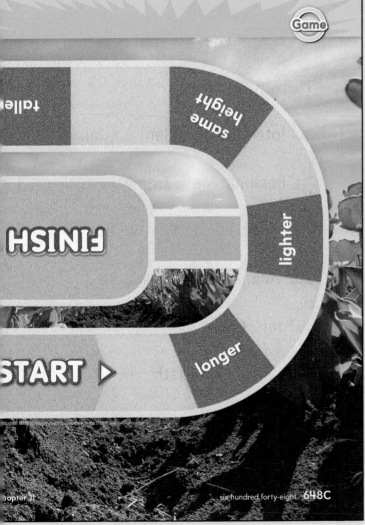

Play the Game

Play this game with children after the content is taught. Read the game directions aloud. Then model how to play the game. Show children how to toss the number cube, read the number rolled, and move a playing piece that many spaces. Demonstrate how to use connecting cubes to show what a term means. For example, model how to use 2 red cubes and 2 blue cubes to show *same length*.

Be sure to explain how a player wins the game and ensure that all children understand how to play.

The measurement words used in this game can also be found in the Chapter Resource book.

The Write Way

These short, informal drawing activities address the vocabulary and content from this chapter. Communicating about math clarifies and deepens children's understandings about math concepts.

Direct children's attention to the drawing box, and read the directions aloud. Give children 5–10 minutes to think about the drawing prompt and draw a response. Encourage them to label their drawings as they are able. When children have completed their drawings, share and discuss the following questions.

- **Does my drawing show that I understand the math idea(s)?**
- **Is my drawing clear and easy to understand?**
- **Do I use math vocabulary to label my drawing?**
- **Do my labels tell more about my drawing?**

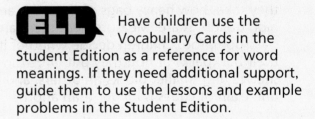 Have children use the Vocabulary Cards in the Student Edition as a reference for word meanings. If they need additional support, guide them to use the lessons and example problems in the Student Edition.

Hands On • Compare Lengths

LESSON AT A GLANCE

FOCUS   COHERENCE   RIGOR

F C R Focus:

Common Core State Standards

○ **K.MD.A.2** Directly compare two objects with a measurable attribute in common, to see which object has "more of"/"less of" the attribute, and describe the difference.

MATHEMATICAL PRACTICES (See *Mathematical Practices in GO Math!* in the *Planning Guide* for full text.)
MP3 Construct viable arguments and critique the reasoning of others.
MP5 Use appropriate tools strategically.
MP6 Attend to precision.

F C R Coherence:

Standards Across the Grades
Grade K   After
K.MD.A.2   1.MD.A.1

F C R Rigor:

Level 1: Understand Concepts....................*Share and Show* (✓ Checked Items)
Level 2: Procedural Skills and Fluency.......*On Your Own, Practice and Homework*
Level 3: Applications.................................*Think Smarter and Go Deeper*

Learning Objective
Directly compare the lengths of two objects.

Language Objective
Pairs of children describe and compare the lengths of two objects.

Materials
MathBoard, connecting cubes

F C R For more about how *GO Math!* fosters **Coherence** within the Content Standards and Mathematical Progressions for this chapter, see page 645H.

About the Math
Professional Development

Why Teach This

Measurement is widely used in everyday life. Children and their families often refer to measurement ideas, such as how much children have grown, the lengths of walks they take, how heavy bags of groceries are, and how high buildings are. Measurement ideas are used in the classroom, too. Children decide whether items will fit in their backpacks or not; they put large blocks on certain shelves and smaller blocks on others; and they see that one train of cubes is longer than another.

Measurement bridges two other important areas of mathematics—geometry and number sense. Children have compared numbers, shapes, and lengths of sides. In this chapter, they will compare lengths, heights, and weights.

 Professional Development Videos

 GO DIGITAL

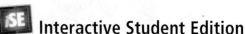 **Interactive Student Edition**

Personal Math Trainer

 Math on the Spot Video

 Animated Math Models

iT *i*Tools: Counters

 HMH Mega Math

Problem of the Day 11.1

Number of the Day **What number is one greater than 12? one greater than 8?** 13; 9

What number is two greater than 10? two greater than 7? 12; 9

Vocabulary **longer, shorter, same length**

Vocabulary Builder

Materials Vocabulary Cards for *longer* and *shorter* (see *eTeacher Resources*)

Longer, Shorter

Show a five-cube train. Trace along its length with your finger. Invite a child to build a cube train that is longer than yours. Invite another child to build a cube train that is shorter than yours. Have them use the vocabulary cards to label the longer and shorter cube trains.

Explain to children that when comparing lengths, both objects need to start at the same point. Show what happens when the cube trains do not start at the same point.

Literature Connection

From the Grab-and-Go™ Differentiated Centers Kit

Children read the book and compare lengths.

Who Am I?

① ENGAGE

with the Interactive Student Edition

Essential Question
How can you compare the lengths of two objects?

Making Connections
Invite children to tell you what they remember about measuring.

What does it mean to measure something? Possible answer: to find out how long or full something is **Why might you measure something?** Possible answer: to make sure you have the right amount of something

Learning Activity
Direct children to think about how to compare objects.

- **What did Scout and Sher find?** pine cones

- **How are the pine cones different?** Answers may vary; one looks bigger, one looks shorter, etc.

- **What does Scout want to know?** which pine cone is longer

Literacy and Mathematics
Choose one or more of the following activities.

- As a class, write a story about a windy day.

- Have children work in pairs to act out the scene, one playing Scout and the other playing Sher.

EXPLORE

Listen and Draw

Read aloud this problem as children listen.

Ling has two pencils. How can she find which is longer and which is shorter?

- **To compare lengths, or find which object is longer or shorter, the objects must start at the same place.**

- **Compare the lengths of the two pencils in the picture. What do you need to check before you can compare the lengths of two objects?** that both objects start at the same place

- **Look at where each pencil ends. Which one is longer?** the one that sticks out farther

- **Which pencil is shorter?** the one that does not stick out as far

MP5 Use appropriate tools strategically.

- **How did you use the line to tell you which pencil was shorter?** Possible answer: Since both pencil points start at the line, I knew the one that ended sooner was shorter.

Have children compare the pencils using the terms *longer than*, *shorter than*, or *about the same length*. Have children trace around the longer pencil. Have them trace the X on the shorter pencil.

Reread the problem about Ling.

MP3 Construct viable arguments and critique the reasoning of others.

- **How could Ling find out which pencil is longer and which is shorter?** She could place the two pencils at the same starting place and compare where each one ends.

ELL **Strategy:**
Identify Relationships

Draw on the board two pencils that are different lengths. Point to the shorter one and say, **This pencil is shorter than that pencil.** Point to the longer one and explain that it is longer.

Repeat with two same-size pencils using *about the same length*.

Direct children's attention to the two pencils on the page. Review their relationship and ask children to point to the pair of pencils on the board that show the same relationship as the pencils on the page.

K.MD.A.2 Directly compare two objects with a measurable attribute in common, to see which object has "more of"/ "less of" the attribute, and describe the difference.

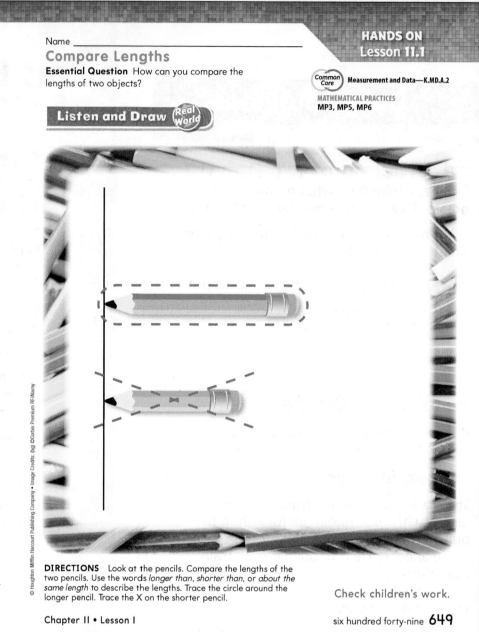

Name _____

Compare Lengths

Essential Question How can you compare the lengths of two objects?

HANDS ON
Lesson 11.1

Common Core Measurement and Data—K.MD.A.2

MATHEMATICAL PRACTICES
MP3, MP5, MP6

Listen and Draw *Real World*

DIRECTIONS Look at the pencils. Compare the lengths of the two pencils. Use the words *longer than, shorter than,* or *about the same length* to describe the lengths. Trace the circle around the longer pencil. Trace the X on the shorter pencil.

Check children's work.

Chapter 11 • Lesson 1

six hundred forty-nine **649**

Reteach 11.1 ▲RtI **Enrich 11.1** **Differentiated Instruction**

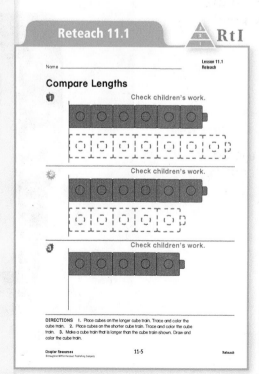

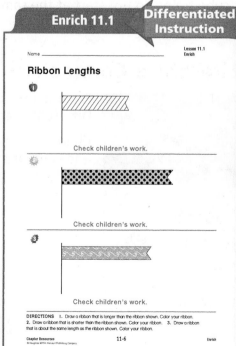

Share and Show

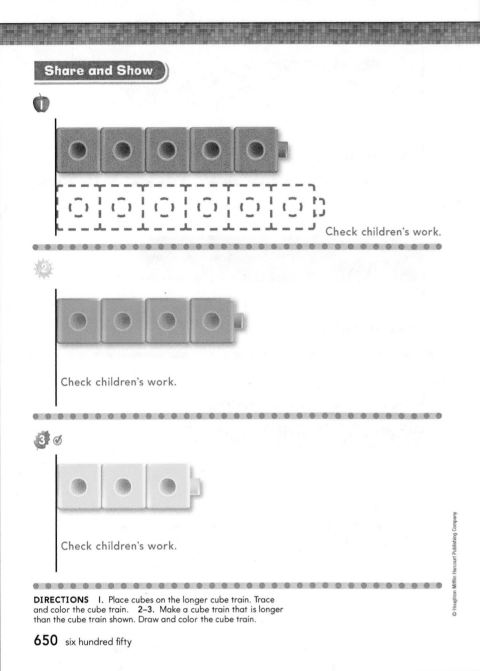

1

Check children's work.

2

Check children's work.

3 ✓

Check children's work.

DIRECTIONS I. Place cubes on the longer cube train. Trace and color the cube train. 2–3. Make a cube train that is longer than the cube train shown. Draw and color the cube train.

650 six hundred fifty

© Houghton Mifflin Harcourt Publishing Company

---

3 EXPLAIN

Share and Show

Materials connecting cubes

For Exercises 1–3, have children use cubes to make longer cube trains.

- **Look at Exercise 1. Place cubes on the longer cube train.**
- **Where will your cube train begin?** at the same line as the red cube train **How many cubes will you use?** 6
- **Look at Exercise 2. How many cubes are in the train?** 4 **How many cubes will you use to make a longer train?** Possible answers: five to eight cubes
- **Look at the yellow cube train in Exercise 3. Make a cube train that is longer. How many cubes did you use?** Possible answers: four to eight cubes

MP6 Attend to precision. Have children compare the cube trains in each exercise, using the term *longer than*, and tell why it is important that each cube train begins at the same point on the page.

Use the checked exercise(s) for Quick Check.

 Quick Check

If ➜ a child misses the checked exercise(s)

Then ➜ Differentiate Instruction with
- Reteach 11.1
- Personal Math Trainer K.MD.A.2
- RtI Tier 1 Activity (online)

! COMMON ERRORS

Error Children may not understand the term *longer*.

Example For Exercise 3, children make a two-cube train.

Springboard to Learning Align two cube trains of different lengths. Have children follow the length of each cube train with a finger and tell which cube train goes out farther. Explain that the cube train that goes out farther is the longer cube train.

Advanced Learners 🕐 Kinesthetic / Visual Partners

Materials small classroom objects

Have each child choose a small, easily-measured item (such as a pencil). Ask partners to trade objects with each other.

Challenge each partner to find a classroom object that is the same length. Tell children that the object they find must be a different kind of object (for example a paintbrush, not a pencil).

Once children find the objects, have them draw both objects, one under the other to check.

Children can share their work with each other and then with the class.

④ ELABORATE

More Practice

For Exercises 4–6, have children use cubes to make, draw, and color shorter cube trains.

- **Look at Exercise 4. Make a cube train shorter than the orange cube train. Where will the cube train begin?** on the same line as the orange cube train **How many cubes did you use?** Possible answers: one to six cubes

Continue with similar questioning for Exercises 5 and 6. Have children share their answers. Discuss why there is more than one possible answer for each exercise.

MP2 Reason abstractly and quantitatively. Read the following problem.

- **Look at the cube train that you made in Exercise 4. How could you make the cube train shorter?** Take away some cubes.

GO DEEPER

MP1 Make sense of problems and persevere in solving them. Read the following problems.

- **Compare the cube trains you made in Exercises 5 and 6. Which one is shorter? Explain.** Children's responses should include that the shorter cube train is the one with fewer cubes.

- **Describe two ways you can make a cube train shorter than the red cube train in Exercise 6.** I can count the cubes in the red cube train and make a train with fewer cubes. I can make a cube train that doesn't stick out as far when the ends of both trains are lined up.

MP6 Attend to precision. Review with children words they could use to compare the lengths of two cube trains.

Math on the Spot Video Tutor
Use this video to help children model and solve this type of *Think Smarter* problem.

 Math on the Spot videos are in the Interactive Student Edition and at *www.thinkcentral.com*.

Name _____

④ ✓

Check children's work.

5

Check children's work.

6

Check children's work.

DIRECTIONS   4–6. Make a cube train that is shorter than the cube train shown. Draw and color the cube train.

Chapter 11 • Lesson 1   six hundred fifty-one **651**

Problem Solving • Applications Real World

WRITE Math

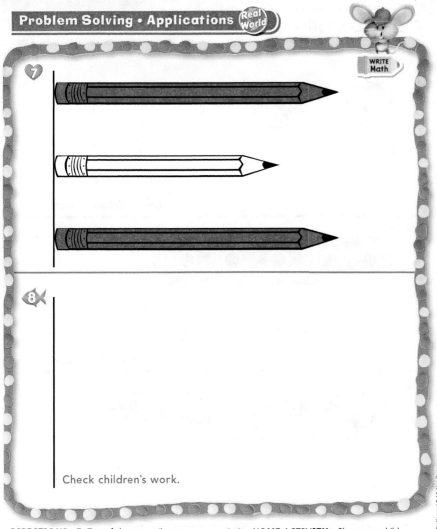

7

8

Check children's work.

DIRECTIONS 7. Two of these pencils are about the same length. Color those pencils. 8. Draw to show what you know about two objects that are about the same length. Tell a friend about your drawing.

HOME ACTIVITY • Show your child a pencil and ask him or her to find an object that is longer than the pencil. Repeat with an object that is shorter than the pencil.

652 six hundred fifty-two

© Houghton Mifflin Harcourt Publishing Company

DIFFERENTIATED INSTRUCTION   INDEPENDENT ACTIVITIES

Grab-and-Go!

Differentiated Centers Kit

Activities *Long and Short*	**Literature** *Who Am I?*	**Games** *Connecting Cube Challenge*
Children complete blue Activity Card 19 by comparing lengths.	Children read the book and compare lengths.	Children investigate and compare lengths of classroom items.

Problem Solving • Applications Real World

Common Core **MATHEMATICAL PRACTICES**

Read the problem for Exercise 7. Discuss the meaning of *about the same length*. Explain that when objects start at the same place and end at about the same place, they are about the same length. Ask children to explain how they will solve the problem.

- **Are all the pencils the same length?** no

MP7 Look for and make use of structure.

- **Which pencils are about the same length?** the top and bottom ones **Color them. How does the middle pencil compare?** It is shorter.

MP1 Make sense of problems and persevere in solving them. For Exercise 8, ask children what the problem is asking them to show in their drawings. Establish that they must show two objects that are about the same length.

MP4 Model with mathematics. Have children suggest objects to draw. Remind them to start each object in the same place.

Math Journal   WRITE) Math

MP6 Attend to precision. After children complete their drawings, invite them to tell a friend about their drawings and use the words *about the same length* to compare the items.

---

5 **EVALUATE** Formative Assessment

Essential Question

Reflect Using the Language Objective Have pairs of children describe and compare to answer the Essential Question.

How can you compare the lengths of two objects? I can put two objects, one under the other, starting at the same place. I can see if one object is shorter than, longer than, or about the same length as the other object.

Practice and Homework

Use the Practice and Homework pages to provide children with more practice of the concepts and skills presented in this lesson. Children master their understanding and begin using critical thinking skills as they complete the practice items.

Compare Lengths

Common Core **COMMON CORE STANDARD—K.MD.A.2**
Describe and compare measurable attributes.

1

Check children's work.

2

Check children's work.

3

Check children's work.

DIRECTIONS 1. Make a cube train that is longer than the cube train shown. Draw and color the cube train. **2.** Make a cube train that is shorter than the cube train shown. Draw and color the cube train. **3.** Make a cube train that is about the same length as the cube train shown. Draw and color the cube train.

© Houghton Mifflin Harcourt Publishing Company

Chapter 11

six hundred fifty-three **653**

Extend the Math Activity

Make a Longer and a Shorter Cube Train

Materials connecting cubes

Investigate Have children make a longer and a shorter cube train than a given cube train and order the cube trains from longest to shortest.

Math Talk Show a three-cube train.

- **If you wanted to build a longer cube train, what would you have to do?** Possible answer: Start with a three-cube train and add some more cubes.

- **If you wanted to build a shorter cube train, what would you have to do?** Possible answer: Start with a three-cube train and take away some cubes.

- **How can you place the cube trains in order from longest to shortest ?** Possible answer: I can put all the cube trains on the same starting line. I can put the cube train that goes out the farthest on

top. Then I can put the cube train that goes out the next farthest in the middle and the shortest cube train last.

Summarize Children should be able to make a longer and shorter cube train than the given cube train and then order the cube trains from longest to shortest.

- See if children can make a longer cube train.

- Watch if children are able to make a shorter cube train.

- Children should demonstrate an understanding of longer and shorter by ordering the cube trains.

- Children should be able to use appropriate vocabulary such as *longer than* and *shorter than* to compare the cube trains.

Lesson Check (K.MD.A.2)

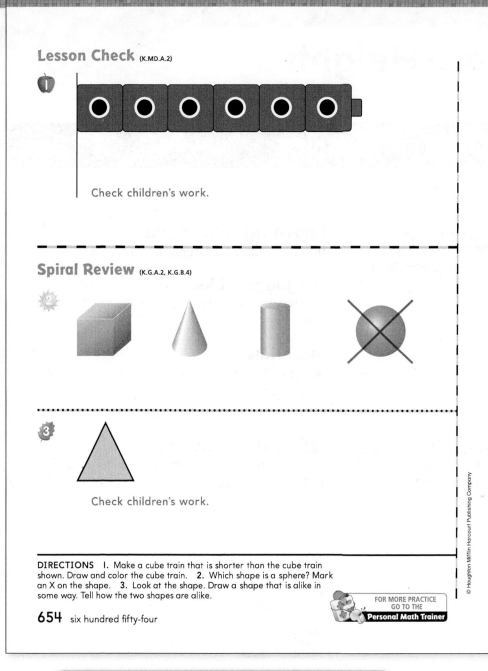

Check children's work.

Spiral Review (K.G.A.2, K.G.B.4)

Check children's work.

Continue concepts and skills practice with Lesson Check. Use Spiral Review to engage children in previously taught concepts and to promote content retention. Common Core standards are correlated to each section.

DIRECTIONS I. Make a cube train that is shorter than the cube train shown. Draw and color the cube train. **2.** Which shape is a sphere? Mark an X on the shape. **3.** Look at the shape. Draw a shape that is alike in some way. Tell how the two shapes are alike.

FOR MORE PRACTICE
GO TO THE
Personal Math Trainer

S.T.E.M. Connecting Math and Science

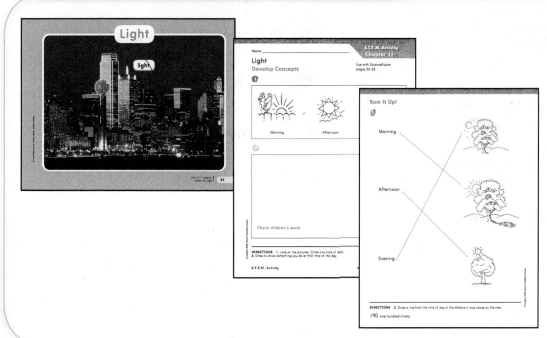

In Chapter 11, children develop their understanding of measurement by comparing the behavior of light during different times of day. These same topics are used often in the development of various science concepts and process skills.

Help children make the connection between math and science through the S.T.E.M. activities and activity worksheets found at www.thinkcentral. com. In Chapter 11, children connect math and science with the S.T.E.M. Activity *Light* and the accompanying worksheets (pages 189 and 190).

Through this S.T.E.M. Activity, children will connect the *GO Math!* Chapter 11 concepts and skills with various activities involving light including matching the shapes of shadows to different times of day. It is recommended that this S.T.E.M. Activity be used after Lesson 11.3.

Hands On • Compare Heights

LESSON AT A GLANCE

FOCUS COHERENCE **RIGOR**

F C R Focus:

Common Core State Standards

○ **K.MD.A.2** Directly compare two objects with a measurable attribute in common, to see which object has "more of"/"less of" the attribute, and describe the difference.

MATHEMATICAL PRACTICES (See *Mathematical Practices in GO Math!* in the *Planning Guide* for full text.)
MP3 Construct viable arguments and critique the reasoning of others.
MP5 Use appropriate tools strategically.
MP6 Attend to precision.

F C R Coherence:

Standards Across the Grades
Grade K   After
K.MD.A.2   1.MD.A.1

F C R Rigor:

Level 1: Understand Concepts....................*Share and Show* (✓ Checked Items)
Level 2: Procedural Skills and Fluency.......*On Your Own, Practice and Homework*
Level 3: Applications...............................*Think Smarter and Go Deeper*

Learning Objective
Directly compare the heights of two objects.

Language Objective
Children role-play how to compare the heights of two objects.

Materials
MathBoard, connecting cubes

F C R For more about how *GO Math!* fosters **Coherence** within the Content Standards and Mathematical Progressions for this chapter, see page 645H.

About the Math
Professional Development

If Children Ask

"How is height different from length?" The answer to this question is more a matter of language than mathematics. Both length and height answer the question, "What is the distance from one point to another?"

You might tell children that length is often used to answer, "How long?" while height is used to answer, "How tall?" The lessons include measuring rules that show what is supposed to be measured or compared.

Point to some classroom objects and indicate with your hands the distance you want children to think about.

 Professional Development Videos

 Interactive Student Edition

 Personal Math Trainer

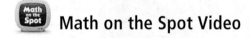 Math on the Spot Video

 Animated Math Models

*i***T** *i*Tools: Counters

GO DIGITAL Problem of the Day 11.2

Word of the Day Hold two cube trains, one in each hand, and tell which is longer than the other.

- **How can you decide which cube train is longer and which is shorter?**
  I can put each cube train to start at the same place and compare to see where each one ends.

Vocabulary taller, same height

GO DIGITAL
- Interactive Student Edition
- Multimedia eGlossary

 Fluency Builder | **Common Core Fluency Standard** K.OA.A.5

Materials Subtraction Fact Cards (within 5), Addition Fact Cards (within 5) (see *eTeacher Resources*)

Subtract/Add Within 5

- Display the subtraction fact card for $5 - 5 = \square$. Tell a subtraction word problem to match the equation and have children act it out. Explain that when the whole set is taken away from the existing set, zero is left.

- Repeat with the addition fact card for $0 + 0 = \square$.

Pages 92–93 in *Strategies and Practice for Skills and Facts Fluency* provide additional fluency support for this lesson.

① ENGAGE

with the Interactive Student Edition

Essential Question
How can you compare the heights of two objects?

Making Connections
Ask children to tell you what they know about length.

Name some things that you think are long. Answers will vary. **Name some things that you think are short.** Answers will vary. **Which is longer, a bicycle or a truck?** a truck

Learning Activity
Guide children about what it means to compare heights.

- **What friend was Scout talking about? How did you figure that out?** Roberto the Robin; possible answer: robins fly and make nests

- **What does Roberto like to do?** sit on the signs

- **Why does Roberto like to sit on the taller sign?** because he can see farther from there

- **What does Scout want to know?** which sign is taller

Literacy and Mathematics
Choose one or more of the following activities.

- Write a class story about comparing two objects.

- Ask children to draw their own picture of the robin on top of a sign. Then have them tell a classmate about their drawing.

② **EXPLORE**

Listen and Draw

Read aloud this problem as children listen.

Ben has two chairs in his room. He wants to give the taller chair to his big sister. If Ben's chairs are like the ones on the page, which chair will he give to his sister?

Ask children to compare the heights of the two chairs. Explain that the height of an object is how tall it is. When comparing the heights of two objects, both should start at the same place. The one that goes higher is taller. Compare heights of classroom objects using the words: *taller, shorter,* or *about the same height.*

- **Which chair in the picture is taller?** the chair on the left **Trace around it.**

- **Which chair in the picture is shorter?** the chair on the right **Trace the X.**

Reread the problem.

- **If Ben's chairs are like the ones on the page, which chair will he give to his sister?** Ben wants to give his sister the taller chair, so he will give her the chair on the left.

MP6 Attend to precision.

- **Describe how Ben might compare the heights of the two chairs. Tell why the way you choose makes sense.** Possible answers: He can place the chairs side by side or back to back on the floor. Since the bottoms of both chairs are on the same level on the floor, he will be able to see which one is taller.

🅴🅻🅻 **Strategy:**
Identify Relationships

Draw two buildings of different heights on the board. Explain their relationship using *taller than* and *shorter than.*

Draw two buildings of the same height and describe them using *about the same height.*

Direct children's attention to the two chairs on the page. Review their relationship and ask children to point to the pair of buildings on the board that show the same relationship as the chairs on the page.

K.MD.A.2 Directly compare two objects with a measurable attribute in common, to see which object has "more of"/"less of" the attribute, and describe the difference.

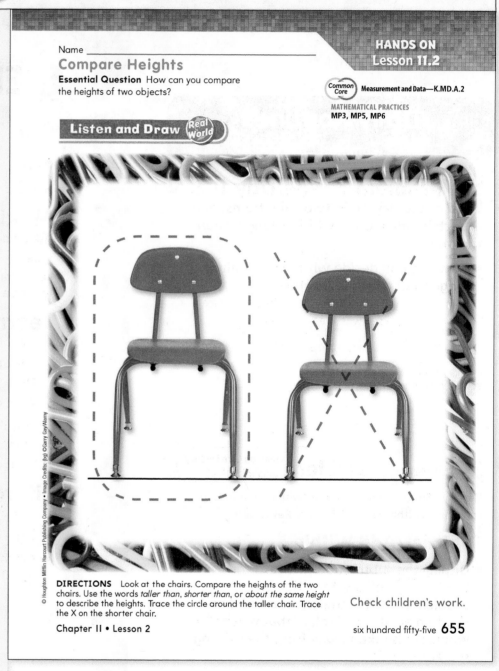

Name _____

HANDS ON
Lesson 11.2

Compare Heights

Essential Question How can you compare the heights of two objects?

Common Core **Measurement and Data—K.MD.A.2**

MATHEMATICAL PRACTICES
MP3, MP5, MP6

Listen and Draw

DIRECTIONS Look at the chairs. Compare the heights of the two chairs. Use the words *taller than, shorter than,* or *about the same height* to describe the heights. Trace the circle around the taller chair. Trace the X on the shorter chair.

Chapter 11 • Lesson 2

Check children's work.

six hundred fifty-five **655**

Reteach 11.2 ▲ **RtI**

Name _____

Lesson 11.2
Reteach

Compare Heights

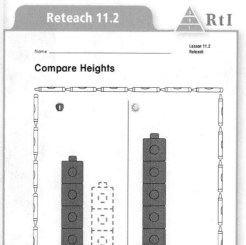

Enrich 11.2 **Differentiated Instruction**

Name _____

Lesson 11.2
Enrich

Shorter and Taller Sunflowers

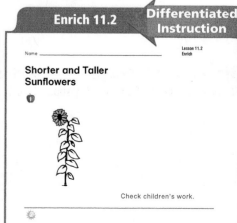

Check children's work.

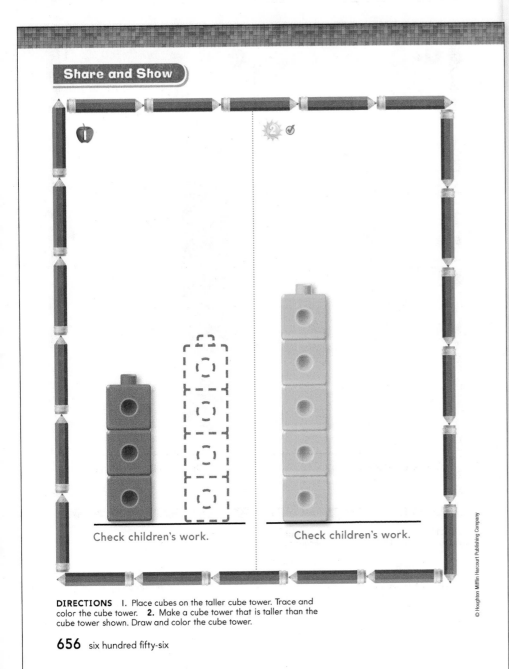

Share and Show

Check children's work.　　　Check children's work.

DIRECTIONS 1. Place cubes on the taller cube tower. Trace and color the cube tower. 2. Make a cube tower that is taller than the cube tower shown. Draw and color the cube tower.

656 six hundred fifty-six

© Houghton Mifflin Harcourt Publishing Company

Share and Show

Materials connecting cubes

For Exercises 1–2, have children use cubes to build cube towers that are taller than the cube tower shown.

MP3 Construct viable arguments and critique the reasoning of others.

- **Look at Exercise 1. How can you tell which cube tower is taller?** Possible answers: I can see which one goes up higher on the page; the cube tower with more cubes is taller.

- **How many cubes will you use?** 4 **Trace and color the cube tower.**

MP5 Use appropriate tools strategically.

- **Look at the cube tower in Exercise 2. Make a cube tower that is taller than the orange cube tower.** Remind children to line up the connecting cubes at the same starting point. Explain that the line on their page will help with lining up their cubes.

- **How many cubes did you use?** Possible answers: six to eight cubes

MP6 Attend to precision. Have children explain how they know their tower is taller.

Use the checked exercise(s) for **Quick Check**.

✔ Quick Check　　RtI

| If | → | a child misses the checked exercise(s) |

| Then | → | **Differentiate Instruction with**
- Reteach 11.2
- Personal Math Trainer K.MD.A.2
- RtI Tier 1 Activity (online) |

Advanced Learners
Visual / Spatial
Individual / Partners

Materials books about animals

Have children browse pictures of animals.

Ask children to draw a grown-up animal and a baby animal and label the pictures with the appropriate word pair: *short/shorter, tall/taller, long/longer.*

tall　　taller

⚠ COMMON ERRORS

Error Children may confuse the terms *longer than* and *taller than*.

Example Children refer to the taller cube tower as "the longer one."

Springboard to Learning Show two cube towers, standing side by side, and identify the taller one. Explain that when you compare two things that are standing, you say *taller* to describe the height.

4 ELABORATE

More Practice

For Exercises 3–4, have children use cubes to build, draw, and color cube towers that are shorter than the cube towers on the page.

- **Look at Exercise 3. Make a cube tower shorter than the yellow cube tower. Where will the cube tower begin?** on the same line as the yellow cube tower **How many cubes did you use?** Possible answers: one to seven cubes

- **For Exercise 4, make a cube tower shorter than the green cube tower. How many cubes did you use?** Possible answers: one to six cubes **Would a cube tower with eight cubes be taller or shorter?** taller

THINK SMARTER

Read this problem to children.

- **Compare the cube towers that you made in Exercises 3 and 4. Write how many cubes are in each tower. Which one is shorter? Explain.** Children's answers should indicate that the shorter cube tower is the one with fewer cubes.

GO DEEPER

MP4 Model with mathematics. Ask children to look at the two cube towers they drew. They can compare them visually to see which one is shorter. They can also count the cubes in each one. Have children write the number of cubes next to each cube tower they drew to help them compare.

MP3 Construct viable arguments and critique the reasoning of others. Have children tell how they know which cube tower they drew is shorter.

Math on the Spot Video Tutor

Use this video to help children model and solve this type of *Think Smarter* problem.

GO DIGITAL **Math on the Spot** videos are in the Interactive Student Edition and at *www.thinkcentral.com*.

Name _____

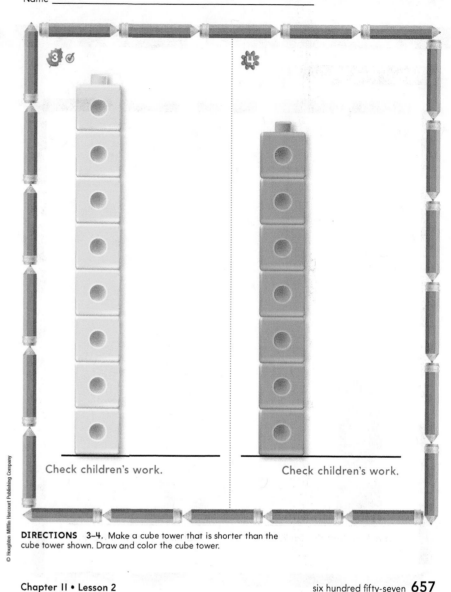

Check children's work.   Check children's work.

DIRECTIONS 3–4. Make a cube tower that is shorter than the cube tower shown. Draw and color the cube tower.

Chapter 11 • Lesson 2   six hundred fifty-seven **657**

© Houghton Mifflin Harcourt Publishing Company

Problem Solving • Applications Real World

WRITE Math

5

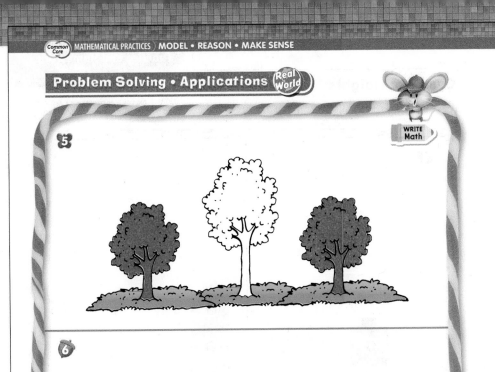

6

Check children's work.

DIRECTIONS 5. Color the trees that are about the same height. **6.** Draw to show what you know about two cube towers that are about the same height. Tell a friend about your drawing.

HOME ACTIVITY • Have your child find two objects, such as plastic toys or stuffed animals. Have him or her place the objects side by side to compare the heights. Ask your child which object is taller and which object is shorter.

658 six hundred fifty-eight

DIFFERENTIATED INSTRUCTION INDEPENDENT ACTIVITIES

Grab-and-Go!
Differentiated Centers Kit

Activities
Ups and Downs!

Children complete orange Activity Card 19 by comparing heights.

Literature
Who Am I?

Children read the book and compare lengths.

Problem Solving • Applications Real World

Common Core MATHEMATICAL PRACTICES

Read Exercise 5. Discuss the meaning of *about the same height*. Explain that when objects start and end at the same place, the objects are about the same height. Ask children to explain how they know which trees are about the same height.

MP7 Look for and make use of structure.

• **How can you describe the heights of the trees?** Two of the trees are about the same height and one is taller than the other two.

• **Which trees are about the same height?** the ones on the outside **Color the trees that are the same height. How does the middle tree compare?** It is taller.

MP1 Make sense of problems and persevere in solving them. For Exercise 6, ask children what the problem is asking them to show in their drawings. Establish that they must show two cube towers that are about the same height.

MP4 Model with mathematics. Remind children to start at the same place when drawing their cube towers.

Math Journal WRITE Math

MP6 Attend to precision. Invite children to share their drawings and use the words *about the same height* to compare the heights of the cube towers that they drew.

---

5 EVALUATE Formative Assessment

Essential Question

Reflect Using the Language Objective Have children role-play how to answer the Essential Question.

How can you compare the heights of two objects? I can put two things side by side, starting at the same place. I can see if one object is shorter than, taller than, or about the same height as the other object.

Practice and Homework

Use the Practice and Homework pages to provide children with more practice of the concepts and skills presented in this lesson. Children master their understanding and begin using critical thinking skills as they complete the practice items.

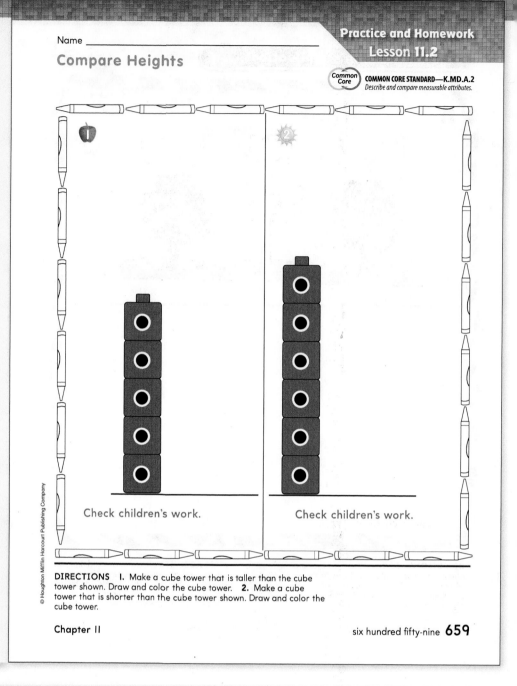

Name _____

Compare Heights

Practice and Homework
Lesson 11.2

COMMON CORE STANDARD—K.MD.A.2
Describe and compare measurable attributes.

Check children's work.

Check children's work.

DIRECTIONS **1.** Make a cube tower that is taller than the cube tower shown. Draw and color the cube tower. **2.** Make a cube tower that is shorter than the cube tower shown. Draw and color the cube tower.

Chapter 11   six hundred fifty-nine **659**

© Houghton Mifflin Harcourt Publishing Company

Math Talk in Action

Teacher:	We compared the heights of similar objects. Now we can compare your height to the height of other things.
Becky:	Can I go first?
Teacher:	Yes, Becky. Find something that is taller than you are.
Becky:	Well, the door is taller than I am.
Teacher:	Good. Can someone else find something that is taller than you?
Angel:	I know! The clock is taller than I am.

Teacher:	The clock is higher than you, but it is not taller. To compare heights, remember to think of both objects starting at the same point and find which one goes up higher.
Angel:	Oh, if the clock is on the ground like me, I am taller. I get it now.
Teacher:	Who can find something that they are taller than?
Sam:	I can. I am taller than my chair.
Teacher:	Well done.

Lesson Check (K.MD.A.2)

1

Check children's work.

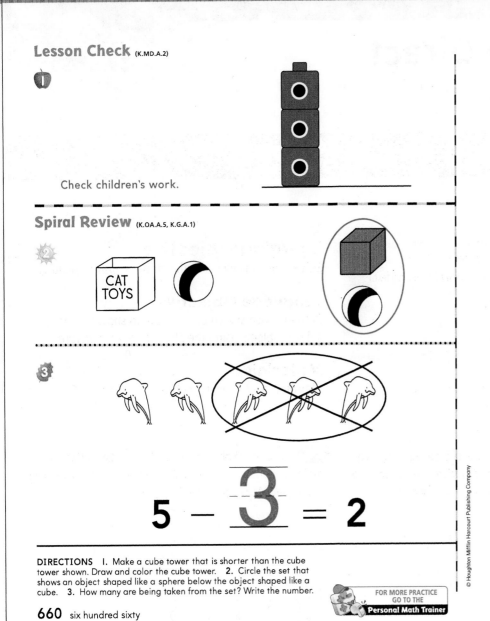

Spiral Review (K.OA.A.5, K.G.A.1)

2

CAT TOYS

3

$$5 - \underline{3} = 2$$

DIRECTIONS 1. Make a cube tower that is shorter than the cube tower shown. Draw and color the cube tower. 2. Circle the set that shows an object shaped like a sphere below the object shaped like a cube. 3. How many are being taken from the set? Write the number.

FOR MORE PRACTICE
GO TO THE
Personal Math Trainer

© Houghton Mifflin Harcourt Publishing Company

660 six hundred sixty

Continue concepts and skills practice with Lesson Check. Use Spiral Review to engage children in previously taught concepts and to promote content retention. Common Core standards are correlated to each section.

Problem Solving • Direct Comparison

LESSON AT A GLANCE

F C R Focus:

Common Core State Standards

○ **K.MD.A.2** Directly compare two objects with a measurable attribute in common, to see which object has "more of"/ "less of" the attribute, and describe the difference.

MATHEMATICAL PRACTICES (See *Mathematical Practices in GO Math!* in the *Planning Guide* for full text.)
MP1 Make sense of problems and persevere in solving them.
MP3 Construct viable arguments and critique the reasoning of others.
MP6 Attend to precision.

F C R Coherence:

Standards Across the Grades

Grade K	After
K.MD.A.2	1.MD.A.1

F C R Rigor:

Level 1: Understand Concepts....................*Share and Show* (✓ Checked Items)
Level 2: Procedural Skills and Fluency.......*On Your Own, Practice and Homework*
Level 3: Applications..................................*Think Smarter and Go Deeper*

Learning Objective
Solve problems by using the strategy *draw a picture*.

Language Objective
Partners each sketch an example to show how to solve problems using the strategy *draw a picture*.

Materials
MathBoard, connecting cubes

F C R For more about how *GO Math!* fosters **Coherence** within the Content Standards and Mathematical Progressions for this chapter, see page 645H.

About the Math

Professional Development

MP1 Make sense of problems and persevere in solving them.

In this lesson, children will be asked to use direct comparison to compare lengths and heights of two objects. They need to analyze what they are being asked and make a plan to solve the problem.

When using direct comparison to compare two objects, children should understand the objects must both be placed at the same starting point whether they are placed horizontally or vertically to compare length or height. Children need to conceptualize the problem by using actual objects or pictures.

Once children have reached an answer, they should ask themselves if their answer makes sense.

 Professional Development Videos

 Interactive Student Edition

 Personal Math Trainer

 Math on the Spot Video

Daily Routines

Common Core

 Problem of the Day 11.3

Word of the Day Look at the two cube trains. Which one is *longer*? Which one is *shorter*? red train; blue train

Have children use the words *longer* and *shorter* to compare two other objects.

Vocabulary

 • Interactive Student Edition
• Multimedia eGlossary

Fluency Builder
Whose Tower is Taller?

Materials red and blue connecting cubes

Distribute connecting cubes to partners. Each partner should get a different color. Have each child work in secret to build a tower. Then ask a series of questions to help them compare the two towers.

- **How can you compare the heights of the two towers?** Stand them up side by side and see which one goes higher.

- **Why is it important to stand the towers on the same, flat place, such as a desk?** When the towers start at the same place you can see which one is taller.

- **Which tower is taller?** Check children's work.

Have children repeat the activity with towers of different heights. This time, have them find the shorter tower.

❶ ENGAGE

with the Interactive Student Edition

Essential Question
How can you solve problems using the strategy *draw a picture*?

Making Connections
Ask children to tell what they know about comparing heights and lengths.

- **When you compare the length or height of two objects, why do you line them up at the same starting place?** You need to be able to see where each object ends.

- **How do you know which of two objects is shorter?** The shorter object does not stick out as far or high. **Longer?** The longer object sticks out farther. **Taller?** The taller one goes higher.

Learning Activity
Guide children to think about strategies they can use to compare objects by height or length.

- **What are some strategies you can use to solve problems?** Possible answers: draw a picture, act it out, make a model

- **How might you use one of those strategies to compare the length of two pencils?** Possible answer: I can trace or draw each pencil as a line and then see which line sticks out farther.

Literacy and Mathematics
View the lesson opener with the children. Then, choose one or more of the following activities:

- Write a class story about comparing length or height.

- Have partners compare the lengths or heights of pairs of classroom objects, and identify which one is shorter.

2 EXPLORE

Unlock the Problem

Materials classroom objects

Read aloud this problem as children listen.

David has two straws of different lengths. How can David compare the straws?

Help children locate objects to complete the page, such as pencils or blocks.

Discuss the black lines on the page. Explain that to make a proper comparison, the ends of both objects must start from the same place.

Discuss how to align the objects along the vertical line to compare length and along the horizontal line to compare height.

- **Line up the ends of both objects on one of the lines.**

Have children draw the objects.

- **How can you see which object is longer than or shorter than the other object?** I can see which drawing goes out farther.

- **How can you see which object is taller than or shorter than the other object?** I can see which drawing goes up farther.

MP1 Make sense of problems and persevere in solving them.

- **What are the ways David can compare the straws?** Possible answers: He can make a drawing of the straws lined up at the left to compare lengths; He can make a drawing of the straws lined up at the bottom to compare the heights.

MP3 Construct viable arguments and critique the reasoning of others. Have children tell a friend about the objects in their drawings, explaining how they know their comparisons are accurate.

ELL Strategy:
Develop Meanings

Use words in context and provide models to develop meaning.

Hold up two pencils aligned horizontally. **Which pencil is longer? Which pencil is shorter?**

Draw a bottle and one that is taller. Have children identify which bottle is taller than or shorter than the other one. Have children draw 2 objects and describe them to a partner using *shorter than* and *longer than*.

K.MD.A.2 Directly compare two objects with a measurable attribute in common, to see which object has "more of"/"less of" the attribute, and describe the difference.

Name _____

Problem Solving • Direct Comparison

Essential Question How can you solve problems using the strategy *draw a picture?*

Common Core — Measurement and Data—K.MD.A.2

MATHEMATICAL PRACTICES
MP1, MP3, MP6

 Unlock the Problem

DIRECTIONS Compare the lengths or heights of two classroom objects. Draw the objects. Tell a friend about your drawing.

Chapter 11 • Lesson 3

Check children's work.

six hundred sixty-one **661**

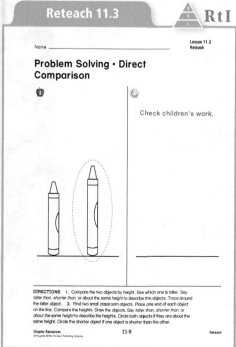

Reteach 11.3 RtI

Name _____
Lesson 11.3 Reteach

Problem Solving • Direct Comparison

Check children's work.

DIRECTIONS 1. Compare the two objects by height. See which one is taller. Say *taller than, shorter than,* or *about the same height* to describe the objects. Trace around the taller object. 2. Find two small classroom objects. Place one end of each object on the line. Compare the heights. Draw the objects. Say *taller than, shorter than,* or *about the same height* to describe the heights. Circle both objects if they are about the same height. Circle the shorter object if one object is shorter than the other.

Chapter Resources 11-9 Reteach

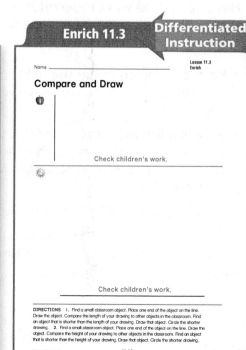

Enrich 11.3 Differentiated Instruction

Name _____
Lesson 11.3 Enrich

Compare and Draw

Check children's work.

Check children's work.

DIRECTIONS 1. Find a small classroom object. Place one end of the object on the line. Draw the object. Compare the length of your drawing to other objects in the classroom. Find an object that is shorter than the length of your drawing. Draw that object. Circle the shorter drawing. 2. Find a small classroom object. Place one end of the object on the line. Draw the object. Compare the height of your drawing to other objects in the classroom. Find an object that is shorter than the height of your drawing. Draw that object. Circle the shorter drawing.

Chapter Resources 11-10 Enrich

Try Another Problem

Check children's work.

DIRECTIONS 1. Find two small classroom objects. Place one end of each object on the line. Compare the lengths. Draw the objects. Say *longer than, shorter than,* or *about the same length* to describe the lengths. Circle both objects if they are about the same length. Circle the longer object if one object is longer than the other.

© Houghton Mifflin Harcourt Publishing Company

662 six hundred sixty-two

③ EXPLAIN

Try Another Problem

Point out and discuss the purpose of the black vertical line on this page.

Have children identify two small classroom objects to compare, such as pencils, crayons, erasers, or chalk.

- **How should you place the objects on the page?** have the ends of each object start at the line on the left side of the page
- **Draw the objects.**

MP6 Attend to precision. Have children use the terms *longer than, shorter than,* or *about the same length* to describe the objects in their drawings. Remind children that when they measure objects across, they are measuring length.

- **Circle the longer object in your drawing.**

MP3 Construct viable arguments and critique the reasoning of others. Have children explain how they know they've located the longer object.

⚠ **COMMON ERRORS**

Error Children may not align their objects on the line.

Example Children place the shorter object so that it extends past the longer one.

Springboard to Learning Have children use a straw or a ruler to help them align the objects. Demonstrate for children how to line up the objects along the edge of the straw to use as a starting place to compare objects.

4 ELABORATE

Share and Show

Have children select two classroom objects to compare by height. Children align the objects and draw them. Ask children to compare the heights of the objects using the words: *taller than*, *shorter than*, or *about the same height*. Have them circle the shorter object.

Use the checked exercise(s) for Quick Check.

Quick Check

If	a child misses the checked exercise(s)
Then	**Differentiate Instruction** with

- Reteach 11.3
- Personal Math Trainer K.MD.A.2
- RtI Tier 1 Activity (online)

 THINK SMARTER

- **How can you compare the heights of two objects if you do not have a page with a line on it?**

GO DEEPER

MP5 Use appropriate tools strategically.
Children can compare objects using a pencil, a straw, or even a ruler to align the ends of the objects.

Math on the Spot Video Tutor
Use this video to help children model and solve this type of *Think Smarter* problem.

 Math on the Spot videos are in the Interactive Student Edition and at *www.thinkcentral.com*.

5 EVALUATE Formative Assessment

Essential Question

Reflect Using the Language Objective
Have pairs of children each sketch an example to answer the Essential Question.

How can you solve problems using the strategy *draw a picture*? I can draw two objects that start on the same line to find which one is longer than, shorter than, or about the same length or height.

Name _____

 Share and Show

Check children's work.

DIRECTIONS 2. Find two small classroom objects. Place one end of each object on the line. Compare the heights. Draw the objects. Say *taller than*, *shorter than*, or *about the same height* to describe the heights. Circle both objects if they are about the same height. Circle the shorter object if one object is shorter than the other.

HOME ACTIVITY • Show your child two objects of different lengths. Have him or her put the ends of the objects on a straight line to compare the lengths and tell which object is shorter and which object is longer.

Chapter II • Lesson 3

six hundred sixty-three **663**

 **DIFFERENTIATED INSTRUCTION**   **INDEPENDENT ACTIVITIES**

Grab-and-Go!

Differentiated Centers Kit

Activities
An Order to Go!

Children complete purple Activity Card 19 by comparing the lengths of three objects.

Literature
Shortest and Longest Where I Live

Children read the book and compare the lengths of household objects.

Games
Connecting Cube Challenge

Children investigate and compare lengths of classroom items.

✓ Mid-Chapter Checkpoint

Personal Math Trainer
Online Assessment
and Intervention

Concepts and Skills

①

Child should draw a cube train with fewer than 6 cubes.

② ③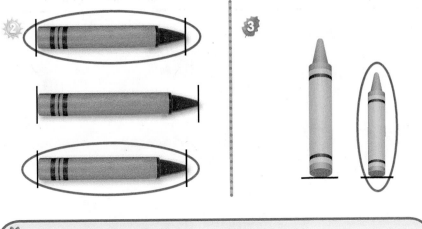

④ THINK SMARTER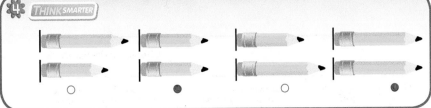

© Houghton Mifflin Harcourt Publishing Company

DIRECTIONS 1. Make a cube train that is shorter than the one shown. Draw the cube train. (K.MD.A.2) 2. Circle the crayons that are about the same length. (K.MD.A.2) 3. Circle the crayon that is shorter. (.K.MD.A.2) 4. Choose all the sets with two pencils that are about the same length. (K.MD.A.2)

664 six hundred sixty-four

Formative Assessment

Use the **Mid-Chapter Checkpoint** to assess children's learning and progress in the first half of the chapter. The formative assessment provides the opportunity to adjust teaching methods for individual or whole class instruction.

THINK SMARTER

This item assesses children's ability to compare the length of two objects. By determining which sets include pencils of the same length, children are also recognizing sets where one pencil is longer or shorter than the other. You may wish to remind children that the black line in each set shows that the pencils start at the same point.

Mid-Chapter Checkpoint

✓ Data-Driven Decision Making ▲ RtI

Based on the results of the Mid-Chapter Checkpoint, use the following resources to strengthen individual or whole class instruction.

Item	Lesson	Standard	Common Error	Personal Math Trainer	Intervene With
1	11.1	K.MD.A.2	May have difficulty identifying objects that are shorter.	K.MD.A.2	R—11.1
2	11.1	K.MD.A.2	May have difficulty identifying objects that are about the same length.	K.MD.A.2	R—11.1
3	11.2	K.MD.A.2	May have difficulty identifying objects that are shorter.	K.MD.A.2	R—11.2
4	11.1	K.MD.A.2	May have difficulty identifying objects that are about the same length.	K.MD.A.2	R—11.1

Key: R—Reteach (in the *Chapter Resources*)

Practice and Homework

Use the Practice and Homework pages to provide children with more practice of the concepts and skills presented in this lesson. Children master their understanding and begin using critical thinking skills as they complete the practice items.

Problem Solving • Direct Comparison

Common Core COMMON CORE STANDARD—K.MD.A.2
Describe and compare measurable attributes.

①

Check children's work.

- -

②

Check children's work.

DIRECTIONS **I.** Find two small classroom objects. Place one end of each object on the line. Compare the lengths. Draw the objects. Say *longer than*, *shorter than*, or *about the same length* to describe the lengths. Circle both objects if they are about the same length. Circle the longer object if one object is longer than the other. **2.** Find two small classroom objects. Place one end of each object on the line. Compare the heights. Draw the objects. Say *taller than*, *shorter than*, or *about the same height* to describe the heights. Circle both objects if they are about the same height. Circle the shorter object if one object is shorter than the other.

© Houghton Mifflin Harcourt Publishing Company

Chapter II   six hundred sixty-five **665**

Lesson Check (K.MD.A.2)

1

Check children's work.

Spiral Review (K.OA.A.2, K.G.B.4)

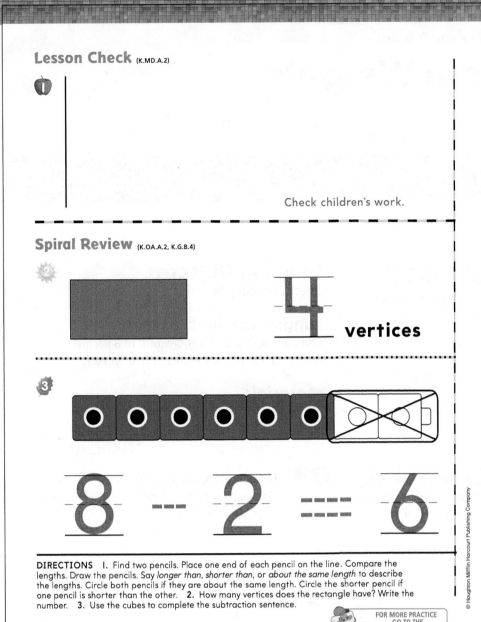

2 4 vertices

3 8 — 2 === 6

© Houghton Mifflin Harcourt Publishing Company

DIRECTIONS 1. Find two pencils. Place one end of each pencil on the line. Compare the lengths. Draw the pencils. Say *longer than, shorter than,* or *about the same length* to describe the lengths. Circle both pencils if they are about the same length. Circle the shorter pencil if one pencil is shorter than the other. 2. How many vertices does the rectangle have? Write the number. 3. Use the cubes to complete the subtraction sentence.

666 six hundred sixty-six

FOR MORE PRACTICE
GO TO THE
Personal Math Trainer

Monitoring Common Core Success

Maintaining Focus on the Major Work

The major work in Grade K involves comparing numbers, K.CC.C. In Lessons 11.1–11.3, children compare lengths and heights. Comparing lengths and heights involves similar problem solving skills to comparing numbers. Children work in Cluster K.CC.C by identifying whether the number of objects in one group, such as a cube train, is *greater than*, *less than*, or *equal to* the number of objects in another group. See Exercises 1–3 on page 650 as an example where children are modeling to show a cube train longer than the cube train shown.

Connecting Content Across Domains and Clusters

In Lessons 11.1–11.3, children connect Cluster K.CC.C of the Domain Counting and Cardinality with Cluster K.MD.A of the Domain Measurement and Data. Given a pair of objects with measurable attributes (length and height), children use their skills with comparing numbers to decide which object is *longer* or *taller* than the other.

Focus on Mathematical Practices

In Lessons 11.1–11.3, children must attend to precision, MP6. Lessons 11.1–11.3 present children with situations in which they carefully formulate explanations. These exercises and word problems test children's ability to draw objects that are "longer," "shorter," "taller," or "shorter". Exercises 1–3 on page 650 are examples of exercises that attend to the full meaning of this mathematical practice. Children also come to understand the importance, when comparing the common attributes of two objects, of starting the objects being compared at the "same point" in order to accurately compute a solution.

Hands On • Compare Weights

LESSON AT A GLANCE

F C R Focus:

Common Core State Standards

○ **K.MD.A.2** Directly compare two objects with a measurable attribute in common, to see which object has "more of"/ "less of" the attribute, and describe the difference.

MATHEMATICAL PRACTICES (See *Mathematical Practices in GO Math!* in the *Planning Guide* for full text.)
MP3 Construct viable arguments and critique the reasoning of others.
MP5 Use appropriate tools strategically.
MP6 Attend to precision.

F C R Coherence:

Standards Across the Grades
Grade K   After
K.MD.A.2   1.MD.A.1

F C R Rigor:

Level 1: Understand Concepts..................*Share and Show* (✓ Checked Items)
Level 2: Procedural Skills and Fluency.......*On Your Own, Practice and Homework*
Level 3: Applications..................................*Think Smarter and Go Deeper*

Learning Objective
Directly compare the weights of two objects.

Language Objective
Children explain and demonstrate to a partner how to compare the weights of two objects.

Materials
MathBoard, classroom objects

F C R For more about how *GO Math!* fosters **Coherence** within the Content Standards and Mathematical Progressions for this chapter, see page 645H.

About the Math
Professional Development

Why Teach This

In this lesson, children hold classroom objects in their hands to compare the weights. They use the words *heavier* and *lighter* as they make decisions comparing the weights of the objects.

Why use real objects? To clarify the weight concept, children must experience it. They must hold objects—ones with discernable differences in weight—in their hands to judge the relative weights. Later, children will develop enough background knowledge to be able to look at pictures of familiar objects and compare their weights.

 Professional Development Videos

 **DIGITAL**

 Interactive Student Edition

 Personal Math Trainer

 Math on the Spot Video

 Animated Math Models

MM HMH Mega Math

Daily Routines

 **Problem of the Day 11.4**

Calendar Math Find and say the date.

What month is it?

What do you think the weather will be like this month?

 Help a child locate the date on the current classroom calendar and lead the class in reading it. Point to the name of the month and have children read it with you.

Vocabulary heavier, lighter, same weight

 • Interactive Student Edition
• Multimedia eGlossary

Fluency Builder
Longer or Taller

Materials connecting cubes in two colors, construction paper

Pair children. Distribute different numbers of connecting cubes, in two different colors, to both partners, so that each partner has a different color. Have each partner make a cube train. Prompt children to compare their cube trains by height and length.

• **First, let's find out which cube train is longer. How can you use the paper to line up the cube trains and see which one is longer?** Line up the cube trains at the edge of the paper and see which one goes farther.

• **Now you want to find out which cube train is taller. How can you use a flat table to figure it out?** You can stand the two cube trains up on the table and see which one goes higher.

Have children find the longer and taller cube train. Repeat the activity with cube trains of different lengths and heights.

---

① ENGAGE

with the Interactive Student Edition

Essential Question
How can you compare the weights of two objects?

Making Connections
Invite children to tell you what they know about comparing things.

• **How can you tell which of two objects is longer or taller than another?** you can compare them

• **What are some ways you can compare things?** Answers may vary; you can put them next to each other, you can measure them, etc.

Learning Activity
Guide children toward thinking about comparing weights.

• **What did Rafferty and Scout find in the bucket?** a leaf and a rock

• **What does Rafferty want to do?** take the lighter object back to her burrow

• **What does Scout want to know?** how to find out which object is lighter

Literacy and Mathematics
Choose one or more of the following activities.

• Have children act out the scene between Scout and Rafferty, making up lines as they go along.

• Tell children that the word *light* has more than one meaning. Make a short list of other multiple meaning words with children and guide them to use the words in brief sentences.

EXPLORE

Listen and Draw

Read aloud this problem as children listen.

Kareem holds a block in one hand and a book in the other. Which object do you think is heavier, the block or the book?

Have a volunteer act out the problem with props. Have other children use the words *lighter than, heavier than,* or *about the same weight* to compare the weights.

- **Which object is** *lighter,* **the block or the book?** the block **Trace the circle.**
- **Which object is** *heavier,* **the block or the book?** the book **Trace the X.**
- **Which object is bigger?** the book
- **Can you think of an object that is bigger than the book, but lighter?** Possible answers: a balloon, a beach ball

MP3 Construct viable arguments and critique the reasoning of others.

- **What can you tell about the size of objects and their weights?** Sometimes a big object can feel light and a small object can feel heavy.

Help children conclude that a small object can be heavy and a big object can be light. Have children give examples, such as a large leaf and a small marble, a sheet of paper and a rock, a poster and a picture frame.

MP6 Attend to precision.

- **What are some ways to describe something that is big?**

ELL **Strategy:**
Identify Relationships

Collect a group of classroom objects.

Have children take turns selecting two objects from the group, holding one in each hand, and using the words *lighter than, heavier than,* or *about the same weight* to compare the weights.

For each pair of objects, ask children which one is bigger and encourage them to describe the relationship between the sizes and the weights of the objects.

667 Chapter 11

K.MD.A.2 Directly compare two objects with a measurable attribute in common, to see which object has "more of"/"less of" the attribute, and describe the difference.

Name _____

Compare Weights

Essential Question How can you compare the weights of two objects?

Measurement and Data—K.MD.A.2

MATHEMATICAL PRACTICES
MP3, MP5, MP6

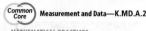

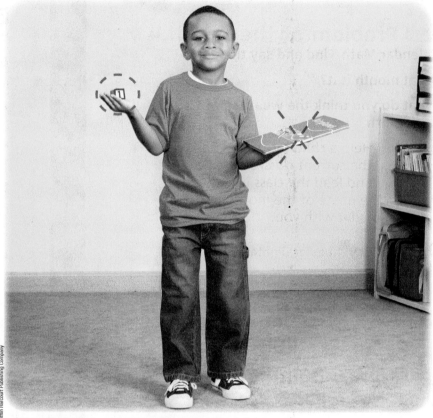

DIRECTIONS Look at the picture. Compare the weights of the two objects. Use the words *heavier than, lighter than,* or *about the same weight* to describe the weights. Trace the circle around the lighter object. Trace the X on the heavier object.

Check children's work.

Chapter 11 • Lesson 4

six hundred sixty-seven **667**

Reteach 11.4 ▲RtI

Name _____

Compare Weights

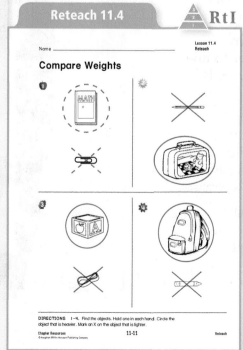

DIRECTIONS 1–4. Find the objects. Hold one in each hand. Circle the object that is heavier. Mark an X on the object that is lighter.

Chapter Resources   11-11   Reteach

Enrich 11.4 **Differentiated Instruction**

Name _____

Kitchen Weights

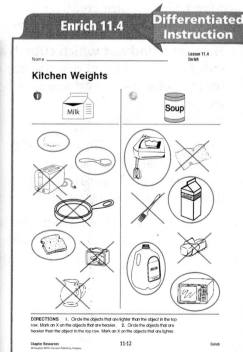

DIRECTIONS 1. Circle the objects that are lighter than the object in the top row. Mark an X on the objects that are heavier. 2. Circle the objects that are heavier than the object in the top row. Mark an X on the objects that are lighter.

Chapter Resources   11-12   Enrich

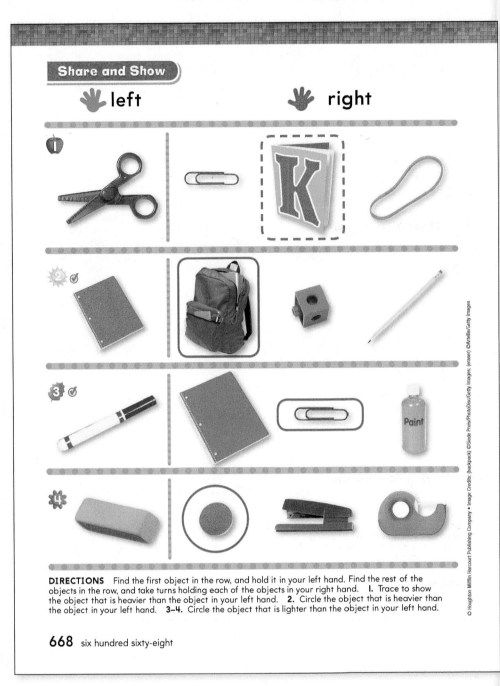

left   right

DIRECTIONS Find the first object in the row, and hold it in your left hand. Find the rest of the objects in the row, and take turns holding each of the objects in your right hand. **I.** Trace to show the object that is heavier than the object in your left hand. **2.** Circle the object that is heavier than the object in your left hand. **3–4.** Circle the object that is lighter than the object in your left hand.

668 six hundred sixty-eight

③ EXPLAIN

Share and Show

Children will need the items on this page. Point to the hands on the page to help children distinguish their own left and right hands. Tell children to think about how heavy the objects are as they hold them.

MP5 Use appropriate tools strategically.

- Look at Exercise 1. Hold a pair of scissors in your left hand. Then hold a paper clip in your right hand. Put the paper clip down and pick up a book. Put the book down and pick up a rubber band.

- Which of the objects that you held in your right hand is heavier than the scissors? the book **Trace around the book.**

Help children work through Exercises 2–4 in a similar way. Use *lighter* for 3 and 4.

MP3 Construct viable arguments and critique the reasoning of others.

- How do you know when an object is heavier? Possible answer: My hand feels like it is being pulled down more.

Use the checked exercise(s) for Quick Check.

✓ Quick Check ▲RtI

If   a child misses the checked exercise(s)

Then   Differentiate Instruction with
- Reteach 11.4
- Personal Math Trainer K.MD.A.2
- RtI Tier 1 Activity (online)

Advanced Learners   🕐 Kinesthetic Partners

Materials classroom objects

Display an assortment of objects of similar and different sizes and different weights.

Have one partner point to two objects and guess which is heavier and which is lighter without holding them.

Have partners take turns holding both objects and talk about whether the guess was correct.

Ask partners to take turns repeating the activity with different objects. Have partners make at least one conclusion based on their findings. Possible answer: A small object can be heavier than a large object.

⚠ COMMON ERRORS

Error Children may confuse the terms *heavier* and *lighter*.

Example In Exercise 2, children identify the pencil as being heavier.

Springboard to Learning Have children hold each of the items in that exercise again. As they hold each pair of items, name the relationship. For example, say, **The backpack is *heavier* than the notebook. The notebook is *lighter* than the backpack.**

Lesson 11.4   668

④ ELABORATE

More Practice

Children will need to find items in the classroom to complete the page. Work through the exercises together. Begin by having children find a book and hold it in one of their hands.

For Exercise 5, have children find an object in the classroom that is lighter than the book and draw it in the workspace.

For Exercise 6, have children find an object in the classroom that is heavier than the book and draw it in the workspace.

 THINK SMARTER

Read the following problem and discuss its solution.

- **Kelly bought two different-sized watermelons. She wants to serve the heavier one. Draw the two watermelons and circle the one she served.**

GO DEEPER

MP6 Attend to precision. Children could discuss that in this case, the larger watermelon weighs more than the smaller one. However, size is not always an indicator of a heavier weight. Ask if anyone can think of something smaller in size being heavier. Possible answer: An acorn is smaller than a feather, but it is heavier than the feather.

MP3 Construct viable arguments and critique the reasoning of others. Challenge children to explain why a bigger watermelon would most likely be heavier than a smaller watermelon, even though bigger objects can be lighter than smaller objects. The two watermelons are the same kind of object.

Math on the Spot Video Tutor

Use this video to help children model and solve this type of *Think Smarter* problem.

GO DIGITAL **Math on the Spot** videos are in the Interactive Student Edition and at *www.thinkcentral.com*.

Chapter 11

Name _____

5

Check children's work.

6

Check children's work.

DIRECTIONS Find a book in the classroom. **5.** Find a classroom object that is lighter than the book. Draw it in the work space. **6.** Find a classroom object that is heavier than the book. Draw it in the work space.

Chapter 11 • Lesson 4   six hundred sixty-nine **669**

© Houghton Mifflin Harcourt Publishing Company

Problem Solving • Applications

7

WRITE Math

Check children's work.

DIRECTIONS 7. Draw to show what you know about comparing the weights of two objects. Tell a friend about your drawing.

 HOME ACTIVITY • Have your child compare the weights of two objects in a house. Then have him or her use the terms *heavier* and *lighter* to describe the weights.

670 six hundred seventy

© Houghton Mifflin Harcourt Publishing Company

 **DIFFERENTIATED INSTRUCTION**   **INDEPENDENT ACTIVITIES**

Grab-and-Go!
Differentiated Centers Kit

Literature
Curious George® and the Mystery Boxes

Children read the book and compare weight and capacity.

Games
Connecting Cube Challenge

 Children investigate and compare lengths of classroom items.

Problem Solving • Applications
Common Core MATHEMATICAL PRACTICES

MP1 Make sense of problems and persevere in solving them. Read the problem. Ask children to explain how they will solve it.

MP4 Model with mathematics. Before children draw to show what they know about comparing weights, establish that their drawing has to show two objects that they can compare by weight. One object should be heavier and one should be lighter. Have children suggest objects to draw.

Math Journal   WRITE Math

MP6 Attend to precision. Invite children to share their drawings and use the terms *heavier* and *lighter* to describe the weights of the objects they drew.

---

5 EVALUATE   Formative Assessment

Essential Question

Reflect Using the Language Objective Have children explain and demonstrate to a partner how to answer the Essential Question.

How can you compare the weights of two objects? I can hold two objects, one in each hand. I can see which one feels heavier and which one feels lighter.

Practice and Homework

Use the Practice and Homework pages to provide children with more practice of the concepts and skills presented in this lesson. Children master their understanding and begin using critical thinking skills as they complete the practice items.

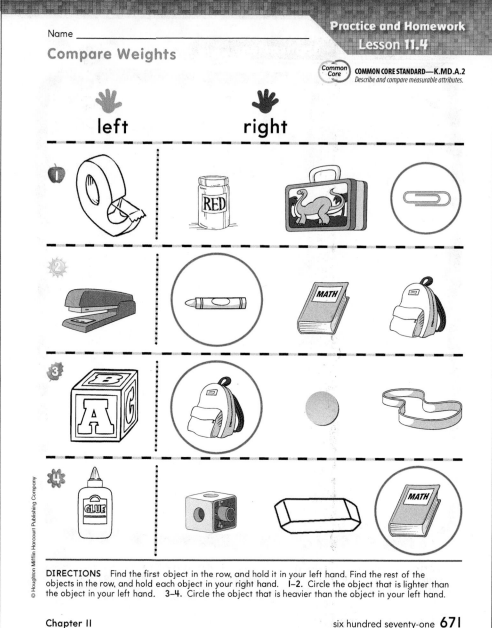

Compare Weights

COMMON CORE STANDARD—K.MD.A.2
Describe and compare measurable attributes.

left   right

DIRECTIONS Find the first object in the row, and hold it in your left hand. Find the rest of the objects in the row, and hold each object in your right hand. **1–2.** Circle the object that is lighter than the object in your left hand. **3–4.** Circle the object that is heavier than the object in your left hand.

© Houghton Mifflin Harcourt Publishing Company

Chapter 11   six hundred seventy-one **671**

Cross-Curricular   S.T.E.M.

Materials identical empty paper cups, water, marbles, cotton balls, sand, and other materials; each labeled with the name of the material

- Explain that scientists measure different attributes of materials to see how they are related.
- Children will compare the other materials to water. Have them take turns holding a cup of a material and the cup of water to compare their weights.
- On the board, make two lists: "Heavier than Water" and "Lighter than Water." As each child makes a comparison, write the results in the correct list.

Heavier than Water	Lighter than Water
marbles	cotton balls
sand	

SOCIAL STUDIES

- Discuss how trucks travel all over our country, bringing people the food they need. Tell children that two trucks of the same size are carrying different kinds of food. They need to decide which truck has the heavier load.

Truck 1	Truck 2	Heavier Load
bags of raw rice	bags of rice cakes	Truck 1
boxes of spinach	boxes of oranges	Truck 2
sacks of fresh corn	sacks of corn flakes	Truck 1

- Have children explain how they decided which load was heavier. Let children suggest loads for the trucks so the class can decide which load is heavier.

Lesson Check (K.MD.A.2)

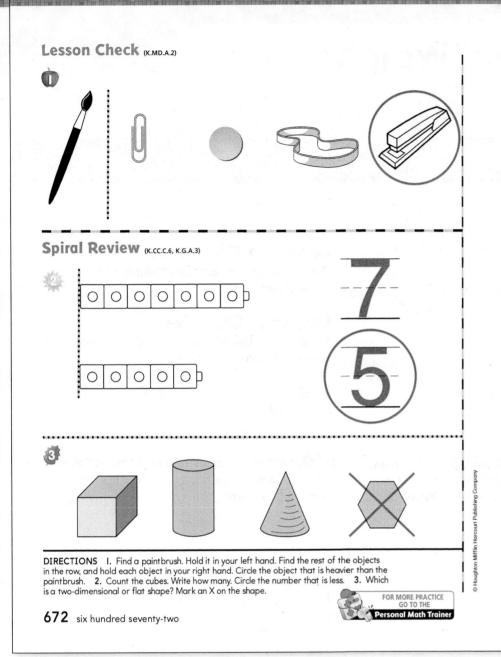

①

Spiral Review (K.CC.C.6, K.G.A.3)

②

$$7$$

$$5$$

③

DIRECTIONS I. Find a paintbrush. Hold it in your left hand. Find the rest of the objects in the row, and hold each object in your right hand. Circle the object that is heavier than the paintbrush. **2.** Count the cubes. Write how many. Circle the number that is less. **3.** Which is a two-dimensional or flat shape? Mark an X on the shape.

FOR MORE PRACTICE
GO TO THE
Personal Math Trainer

Continue concepts and skills practice with Lesson Check. Use Spiral Review to engage children in previously taught concepts and to promote content retention. Common Core standards are correlated to each section.

Length, Height, and Weight

LESSON AT A GLANCE

F C R Focus:

Common Core State Standards

○ **K.MD.A.1** Describe measurable attributes of objects, such as length or weight. Describe several measurable attributes of a single object.

MATHEMATICAL PRACTICES (See *Mathematical Practices in GO Math!* in the *Planning Guide* for full text.)
MP1 Make sense of problems and persevere in solving them.
MP3 Construct viable arguments and critique the reasoning of others.
MP6 Attend to precision.

F C R Coherence:

Standards Across the Grades
Grade K   After
K.MD.A.1   1.MD.A.1

F C R Rigor:

Level 1: Understand Concepts....................*Share and Show* (✓ Checked Items)
Level 2: Procedural Skills and Fluency.......*On Your Own, Practice and Homework*
Level 3: Applications................................*Think Smarter and Go Deeper*

Learning Objective
Describe several measurable attributes of a single object.

Language Objective
Teams of 3–4 children draw and describe three ways you can measure one object.

Materials
MathBoard

F C R For more about how *GO Math!* fosters **Coherence** within the Content Standards and Mathematical Progressions for this chapter, see page 645H.

About the Math
Professional Development

Teaching for Depth

Children have been learning about different ways to compare objects. They have used different measuring techniques to measure different attributes. By now they should realize that objects can be measured in different ways.

Children should understand that a single object can have measurements of height, length, and weight. In this lesson, children will measure to find the length or height of an object. They will also discuss measuring objects by weight.

These skills build the foundation for using units of measure in later grades and in real life to measure objects by inches, centimeters, ounces, or pounds.

 Professional Development Videos

 **Interactive Student Edition**

 **Personal Math Trainer**

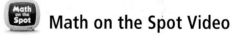 **Math on the Spot Video**

Daily Routines

Common Core

 Problem of the Day 11.5

Word of the Day Look at the two cube towers.

- **Which one is** *taller*? yellow tower
- **Which one is** *shorter*? orange tower

Have children use the words *taller* and *shorter* to compare the heights of two other objects.

Vocabulary

 • Interactive Student Edition
• Multimedia eGlossary

 Fluency Builder | **Common Core Fluency Standard** K.OA.A.5
Add Within 5

Materials Addition Fact Cards (within 5) (see *eTeacher Resources*)

Provide each child with an addition fact card. Allow a moment for children to solve the card they have.

- **If you have a card with an answer of 4, raise your card so that everyone can see.**
  $2 + 2, 1 + 3, 3 + 1, 4 + 0, 0 + 4$

Check children's fact cards. Look for any fact cards children may have raised with a different sum.

Repeat the activity with other sums within 5.

Pages 120–121 in *Strategies and Practice for Skills and Facts Fluency* provide additional fluency support for this lesson.

---

① ENGAGE

with the Interactive Student Edition

Essential Question
How can you describe several ways to measure one object?

Making Connections
Ask children to tell what they know about measuring objects.

- **When you decide which of two objects is shorter or longer, what are you comparing?** length
- **Keenan says his block tower is taller than Ellen's. What is he comparing?** height
- **What are you comparing when you find out if an object is lighter or heavier?** weight

Learning Activity
Guide children to think about the properties of objects. Ask the following questions.

- **What is** *length*? how long something is from side to side
- **What is** *height*? how tall or short something is
- **What is** *weight*? how light or heavy something is

Literacy and Mathematics
View the lesson opener with the children. Then, choose one or more of the following activities:

- Have children choose a classroom object and tell about its length, height, or weight.
- Have partners exchange a short dialogue about a trip to the supermarket or other store in which they use the words *length*, *height*, and *weight*.

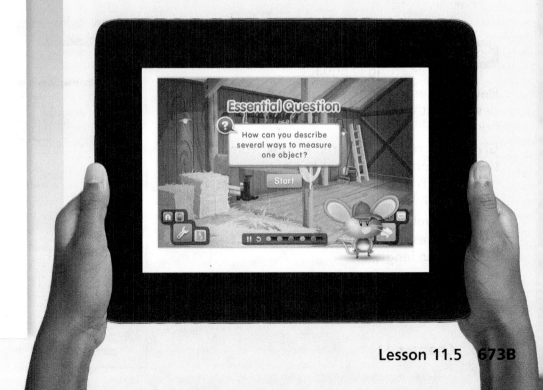

② **EXPLORE**

Listen and Draw

Read the problem aloud as children listen.

Tom and Kim want to measure their books in different ways. What are the ways they can measure their books?

Have children look at the book and the lines on the page. Explain that the lines show how to measure length and height.

Point to the horizontal line and read the word *length*. Discuss its meaning.

MP6 Attend to precision.

• **Trace your finger over the line that shows how to measure the length of the book. How would you describe this line?** Possible answer: It goes from side to side.

Point to the vertical line and read the word *height*. Discuss its meaning.

MP6 Attend to precision.

• **Trace your finger over the line that shows how to measure the height of the book. How would you describe this line?** Possible answer: It goes from bottom to top.

• **Can you think of another way to measure the book?** by weight

Demonstrate picking up a book and describing it as heavy or light.

Reread the problem about Tom and Kim.

MP1 Make sense of problems and persevere in solving them.

• **How can Tom and Kim measure their books?** They can measure their books by length, by height, and by weight.

ELL **Strategy:**
Scaffold Language

Help children practice their comprehension by describing the length, height and weight of books.

Give each group of children a book from the classroom. Review that the book can be measured in different ways: length, height, and weight.

Have a member of the group demonstrate how to measure the book by length and describe the length.

Repeat with height and weight.

Common Core K.MD.A.1 Describe measurable attributes of objects, such as length or weight. Describe several measurable attributes of a single object.

Name _____

Lesson 11.5

Length, Height, and Weight

Essential Question How can you describe several ways to measure one object?

Common Core Measurement and Data—K.MD.A.1

MATHEMATICAL PRACTICES
MP1, MP3, MP6

Listen and Draw

DIRECTIONS Look at the book. Trace your finger over the line that shows how to measure the height of the book. Trace your finger over the line that shows how to measure the length of the book. Talk about another way to measure the book.

Chapter 11 • Lesson 5

Check children's work.

six hundred seventy-three **673**

Reteach 11.5 ▲ **RtI**

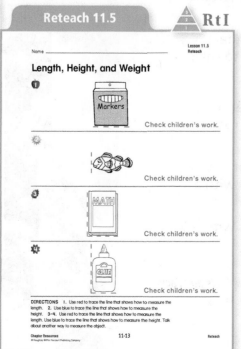

Enrich 11.5 **Differentiated Instruction**

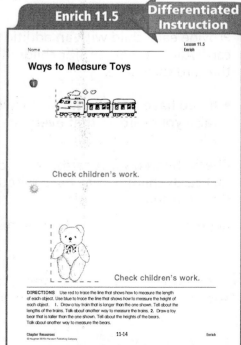

Share and Show

Check children's work.

Check children's work.

DIRECTIONS 1–2. Use red to trace the line that shows how to measure the length. Use blue to trace the line that shows how to measure the height. Talk about another way to measure the object.

© Houghton Mifflin Harcourt Publishing Company

Share and Show

Materials red and blue crayons

Have children locate the tape dispenser in Exercise 1. Point out the dashed lines at the bottom and side of the tape dispenser.

- **Which line shows how to measure the length of the tape dispenser?** Possible answer: the line that goes from side to side **Use red to trace this line.**

- **Which line shows how to measure the height of the tape dispenser?** Possible answer: the line that goes from bottom to top **Use blue to trace this line.**

- **Is there another way to measure the tape dispenser?** by weight

MP3 Construct viable arguments and critique the reasoning of others. Guide children through Exercise 2. Remind children that the lines on the page are there to show them how to measure. As they complete the exercise, have them explain why they colored each line as they did.

 COMMON ERRORS

Error Children may confuse length and height.

Example Children color the wrong line red.

Springboard to Learning Remind children that lines showing length run side to side. Have them finger trace that line. Then tell them that lines going from bottom to top show height. Have them finger trace that line.

Lesson 11.5 674

4 ELABORATE

More Practice

Materials red and blue crayons

For Exercise 3, call attention to the dashed lines around the backpack.

- **Which line shows how to measure the length of the backpack?** the line that goes from side to side **Use red to trace that line.**
- **Which line shows how to measure the height of the backpack?** the line that goes from bottom to top **Use blue to trace that line.**

Ask similar questions for Exercises 4–6. Children should discuss how they can measure by weight.

Use the checked exercise(s) for Quick Check.

 **THINK SMARTER**

- **Draw a book.**
- **Use red to draw the line that shows how to measure the length.**
- **Use blue to draw the line that shows how to measure the height.**

 GO DEEPER

MP3 Construct viable arguments and critique the reasoning of others. Children should discuss attributes that are measurable, such as distance around the book. Encourage them to think about attributes that cannot be measured, such as color and number of pages. Discuss the differences between attributes that can and cannot be measured.

 **Math on the Spot Video Tutor**
Use this video to help children model and solve this type of *Think Smarter* problem.

 Math on the Spot videos are in the Interactive Student Edition and at *www.thinkcentral.com*.

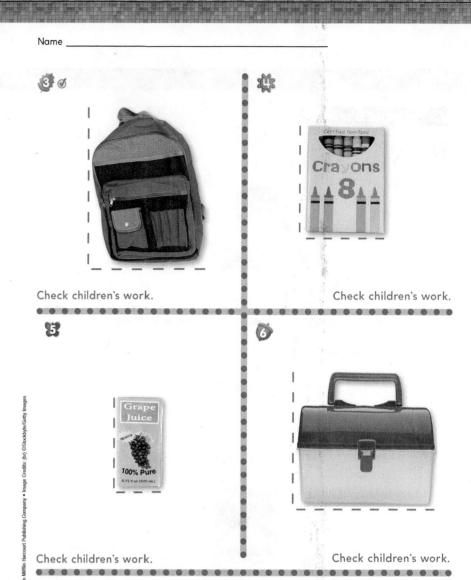

Name _____

3 ✓

Check children's work.

4

Check children's work.

5

Check children's work.

6

Check children's work.

DIRECTIONS 3–6. Use red to trace the line that shows how to measure the length. Use blue to trace the line that shows how to measure the height. Talk about another way to measure the object.

Chapter 11 • Lesson 5   six hundred seventy-five **675**

Problem Solving • Applications

Check children's work.

DIRECTIONS 7. Draw to show what you know about measuring an object in more than one way.

 HOME ACTIVITY • Show your child an object in the house that can be easily measured by length, height, and weight. Ask him or her to describe the different ways to measure the object.

© Houghton Mifflin Harcourt Publishing Company

676 six hundred seventy-six

 DIFFERENTIATED INSTRUCTION **INDEPENDENT ACTIVITIES**

Differentiated Centers Kit

Activities	Literature	Games
Ups and Downs!	**Curious George® and the Mystery Boxes**	**Connecting Cube Challenge**

Children complete orange Activity Card 19 by comparing heights.	Children read the book and compare weight and capacity.	Children investigate and compare lengths of classroom items.

Problem Solving • Applications
Common Core **MATHEMATICAL PRACTICES**

MP1 Make sense of problems and persevere in solving them. After you read the problem, ask children to summarize what they are expected to do.

Have children draw objects to show what they know about measuring by length and by height. Remind children to draw a horizontal line to show length and a vertical line to show height.

MP3 Construct viable arguments and critique the reasoning of others. Have children explain why their drawings show about measuring an object in more than one way.

Math Journal  Math

MP6 Attend to precision. Invite children to share their drawings, describing how they measured by length and height, and then discuss with a friend that objects can also be measured by weight.

⑤ EVALUATE Formative Assessment

Essential Question

Reflect Using the Language Objective Have teams of 3–4 children draw and describe to answer the Essential Question.

How can you describe several ways to measure one object? I can measure the length of an object by going from side to side. I can measure the height of an object by going from bottom to top. I can measure the weight of an object by holding it to see if it is heavy or light.

Practice and Homework

Use the Practice and Homework pages to provide children with more practice of the concepts and skills presented in this lesson. Children master their understanding and begin using critical thinking skills as they complete the practice items.

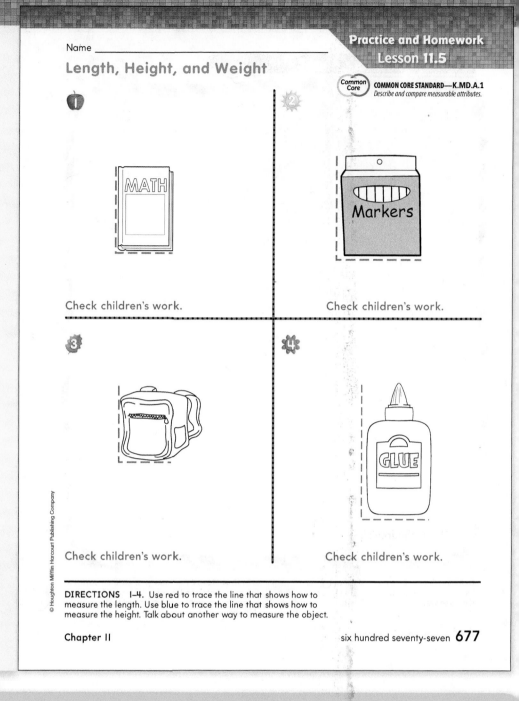

Name _____

Length, Height, and Weight

COMMON CORE STANDARD—K.MD.A.1
Describe and compare measurable attributes.

1 MATH

Check children's work.

2 Markers

Check children's work.

3

Check children's work.

4 GLUE

Check children's work.

DIRECTIONS 1–4. Use red to trace the line that shows how to measure the length. Use blue to trace the line that shows how to measure the height. Talk about another way to measure the object.

Chapter 11

six hundred seventy-seven **677**

© Houghton Mifflin Harcourt Publishing Company

Mathematical Practices in Your Classroom

CCSS.Math.Practice.MP6 Attend to precision.

Communication is an important part of mathematics.

- Giving correct answers is helpful but is only part of what children need to do in the classroom. They also need to use clear definitions in discussions to be able to explain how they arrived at their answers.
- Having children accurately discuss and define how to measure length, height, and weight in this lesson will lay a foundation for measuring objects using standard units in upper grades.
- When asking children to explain how they solved the problems in this lesson, encourage them to use precise language appropriate to the problem, so their answers are easily understood by classmates.

Remind children to use clear, accurate, and precise language in class discussions.

- **How would you explain to a classmate the best way to measure the length of objects?** To measure length, start at one side of the object and go across the object to the other side.
- **How would you explain to a classmate the best way to measure the height of objects?** To measure height, start at the bottom of the object and go up the object to the top.
- **How can you measure the weight of objects?** I can pick up two objects, one in each hand, and feel which is heavier or lighter than the other.

Lesson Check (K.MD.A.1)

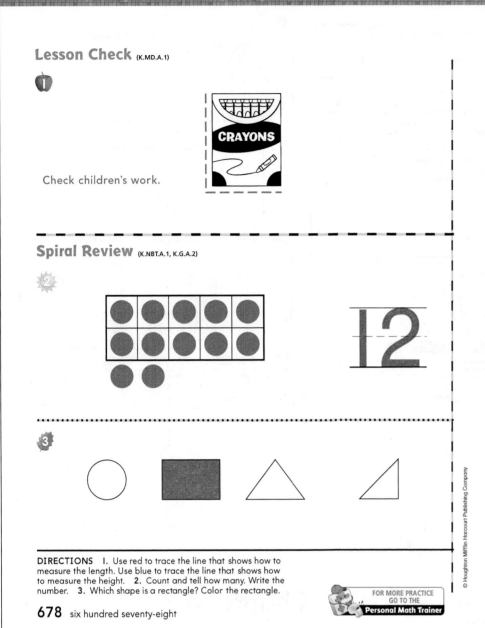

Check children's work.

Spiral Review (K.NBT.A.1, K.G.A.2)

DIRECTIONS **1.** Use red to trace the line that shows how to measure the length. Use blue to trace the line that shows how to measure the height. **2.** Count and tell how many. Write the number. **3.** Which shape is a rectangle? Color the rectangle.

678 six hundred seventy-eight

FOR MORE PRACTICE
GO TO THE
Personal Math Trainer

© Houghton Mifflin Harcourt Publishing Company

Monitoring Common Core Success

Maintaining Focus on the Major Work

The major work in Grade K involves comparing numbers, K.CC.C. In Lessons 11.4–11.5, children compare lengths, heights, and weights. Children work in Cluster K.CC.C by identifying whether the number of objects in one group, such as the number of cars on a toy train, is greater than, less than, or equal to the number of objects in another group. See Enrich Exercise 1 on page 673.

Connecting Content Across Domains and Clusters

In Lessons 11.4 and 11.5, children connect Cluster K.CC.C of the Domain Counting and Cardinality with Cluster K.MD.A of the Domain Measurement and Data. In Lesson 11.4 children use their comparing skills to directly compare two objects with a measurable attribute in common, to see which object has "more of"/"less of" the attribute, and describe the difference, K.MD.A.2. In Lesson 11.5 children describe several measurable attributes of a single object, K.MD.A.1.

Focus on Mathematical Practices

In Lessons 11.4 and 11.5, children frequently construct viable arguments and critique the reasoning of others, MP3. As children learn to compare the weight of two objects, they are required to explain their reasoning. Children use the concept of size to help support their answers, but understand that *larger* does not always mean *heavier*. The Problem Solving exercise on TE page 670 attends to the full meaning of this standard, as children draw two objects, compare them, discuss the problem, and explain it to a friend.

Summative Assessment

Use the **Chapter 11 Review/Test** to assess children's progress in Chapter 11. You may want to review with children the essential question for the chapter.

Chapter Essential Question

How can comparing objects help you measure them?

- How can you compare the length of objects?
- How can you compare the height of objects?
- How can you compare the weight of objects?

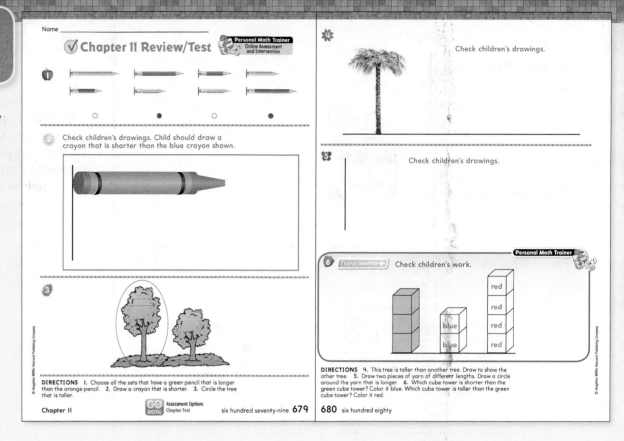

 Data-Driven Decision Making 🔺 RtI Chapter 11

Based on the results of the Chapter Review/Test use the following resources to review skills.

Item	Lesson	Standard	Content Focus	Personal Math Trainer	Intervene With
1	11.1	K.MD.A.2	Compare lengths.	K.MD.A.2	R—11.1
2	11.1	K.MD.A.2	Compare lengths.	K.MD.A.2	R—11.1
3	11.2	K.MD.A.2	Compare heights.	K.MD.A.2	R—11.2
4	11.2	K.MD.A.2	Compare heights.	K.MD.A.2	R—11.2
5	11.3	K.MD.A.2	Draw to compare lengths.	K.MD.A.2	R—11.3
6	11.3	K.MD.A.2	Draw to compare heights.	K.MD.A.2	R—11.3
7, 8, 11, 12	11.4	K.MD.A.2	Compare weights.	K.MD.A.2	R—11.4
9, 10	11.5	K.MD.A.1	Identify ways to measure objects.	K.MD.A.1	R—11.5

Key: **R**—Reteach (in the *Chapter Resources*)

Name _____

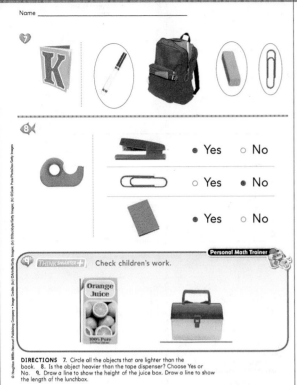

7

8
- Yes ○ No
○ Yes ● No
● Yes ○ No

9 THINK SMARTER ✚ Check children's work.

Orange Juice
100% Pure

10
Crayons 8
Craons 8
Craons 8
Craons 8
○ ● ○ ●

11 Check children's work.

12 Check children's drawings.

DIRECTIONS 7. Circle all the objects that are lighter than the book. 8. Is the object heavier than the tape dispenser? Choose Yes or No. 9. Draw a line to show the height of the juice box. Draw a line to show the length of the lunchbox.

Chapter 11   six hundred eighty-one **681**

DIRECTIONS 10. Choose all of the pictures that have lines that show how to measure height. 11. Look at the objects. Mark an X on the lighter object. Circle the heavier object. 12. Draw an object that is heavier than the pencil.

682 six hundred eighty-two

Performance Assessment Tasks
Chapter 11

See the *Chapter Resources* for a Performance Task that assesses children's understanding of the content of this chapter.

For each task, you will find sample student work for each of the response levels in the task scoring rubric.

Portfolio Performance Assessment Tasks may be used for portfolios.

THINK SMARTER ✚
Personal Math Trainer

Be sure to assign children Exercise 6 in the Personal Math Trainer. It features a video to help children model and solve the problem. This item assesses children's ability to compare the heights of two cube towers, which in one case are not next to each other. Children who incorrectly color the towers may be confusing the terms *taller* and *shorter*. Illustrating comparative height with hand gestures may help children understand the terminology and concepts.

The Personal Math Trainer for Exercise 9 features an animation to help children model and solve the problem. Children should recognize that the juice box and the lunchbox each have height and length. Some children may incorrectly indicate height with a horizontal line and length with a vertical line. Demonstrate that height goes from bottom to top, and length goes from side to side.

Chapter 11 Review/Test   681–682

Chapter 11
Test

Summative Assessment

Use the **Chapter Test** to assess children's progress in Chapter 11.

Chapter tests are presented in Common Core assessment format in the *Chapter Resources.*

Personal Math Trainer

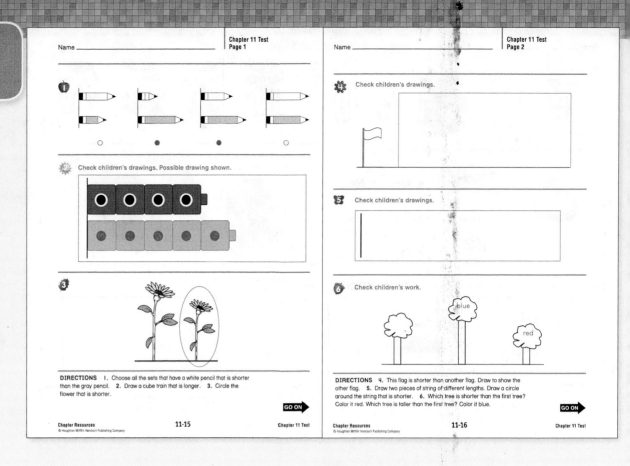

✓ Data-Driven Decision Making ▲RtI

Based on the results of the Chapter Test use the following resources to review skills.

Item	Lesson	Standard	Content Focus	Personal Math Trainer	Intervene With
1	11.1	K.MD.A.2	Compare lengths.	K.MD.A.2	R—11.1
2	11.1	K.MD.A.2	Compare lengths.	K.MD.A.2	R—11.1
3	11.2	K.MD.A.2	Compare heights.	K.MD.A.2	R—11.2
4	11.2	K.MD.A.2	Compare heights.	K.MD.A.2	R—11.2
5	11.3	K.MD.A.2	Draw to compare lengths.	K.MD.A.2	R—11.3
6	11.3	K.MD.A.2	Draw to compare heights.	K.MD.A.2	R—11.3
7, 8, 11, 12	11.4	K.MD.A.2	Compare weights.	K.MD.A.2	R—11.4
9, 10	11.5	K.MD.A.1	Identify ways to measure objects.	K.MD.A.1	R—11.5

Key: **R**—Reteach (in the *Chapter Resources*)

Name _____

Chapter 11 Test
Page 3

Name _____

Chapter 11 Test
Page 4

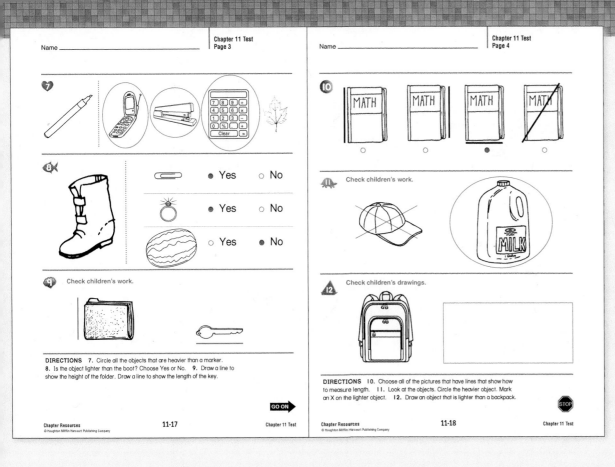

7

8
• Yes ○ No
• Yes ○ No
○ Yes • No

9 Check children's work.

10
MATH MATH MATH MATH
○   ○   •   ○

11 Check children's work.

12 Check children's drawings.

DIRECTIONS 7. Circle all the objects that are heavier than a marker.
8. Is the object lighter than the boot? Choose Yes or No. 9. Draw a line to
show the height of the folder. Draw a line to show the length of the key.

GO ON

DIRECTIONS 10. Choose all of the pictures that have lines that show how
to measure length. 11. Look at the objects. Circle the heavier object. Mark
an X on the lighter object. 12. Draw an object that is lighter than a backpack.

STOP

Chapter Resources
© Houghton Mifflin Harcourt Publishing Company
11-17
Chapter 11 Test

Chapter Resources
© Houghton Mifflin Harcourt Publishing Company
11-18
Chapter 11 Test

Portfolio **Portfolio Suggestions**
The portfolio represents the
growth, talents, achievements,
and reflections of the
mathematics learner. Children
might spend a short time
selecting work samples
for their portfolios.

You may want to have
children respond to the
following questions:

- **How do you think you did
  on this test?**
- **What would you like to
  learn more about?**

For information about how
to organize, share, and
evaluate portfolios, see the
Chapter Resources.

Chapter 11 Test

Chapter 11 Test   682B